gems

jewels &

treasures

STEPHEN SPIGNESI

gems

jewels

&

treasures

THE COMPLETE JEWELRY BOOK

QVC PUBLISHING, INC.

FOR BARBARA WHITE
WITH AFFECTION AND GRATITUDE

QVC Publishing Inc.

Jill Cohen, *Vice President and Publisher*
Ellen Bruzelius, *General Manager*
Sarah Butterworth, *Editorial Director*
Karen Murgolo, *Director of Rights and Acquisitions*
Cassandra Reynolds, *Publishing Assistant*

Produced in association with Patrick Filley Associates, Inc.

Designed by Salsgiver Coveney Associates Inc.

Published by QVC Publishing Inc.,
50 Main Street, Suite 201, Mt. Kisco, New York 10549.

Manufactured in Hong Kong

ISBN 1-928998-32-1

First Edition
10 9 8 7 6 5 4 3 2 1

Front jacket: ©Genevieve Naylor/CORBIS
Back jacket: Carlos Alejandro and
Gemological Institute of America.

All jewelry shown on pages 10-95 photographed by
Carlos Alejandro except that shown on pages 49, 53,
and 73, which is reproduced with permission from
the Gemological Institute of America.

All gemstones shown on pages 10-95 are reproduced with
permission from the Gemological Institute of America.
Necklace on page 21 photographed by Shane McClure © GIA.

All diamonds shown on pages 104-107 are reproduced
with permission from the Diamond Information Center,
except page 106, which is photographed by Carlos Alejandro.

All pearls shown on pages 115-124 photographed by
Carlos Alejandro except 122 top, which is photographed
by William Rutledge.

All precious metals shown on pages 129, 136, 137 left,
141-143, 145-148 bottom, 149 photographed by
Carlos Alejandro except that shown on pages 130-132,
134, 137 right, 138, which is reproduced with permission
from the World Gold Council and 148 top, which is
reproduced with permission from the Platinum Guild
International USA Jewelry, Inc.

Chapter opening photos on pages 8 and 112,
The Kobal Collection; pages 66 and 126, Photofest;
page 96, ©Genevieve Naylor/CORBIS.

*The author and publishers would also like to thank the following
for permission to photograph their jewelry designs:*

J. J. Marco Studio Collection page 17 bottom
Roderick Tenorio page 63
Judith Jack Reflections Collection page 85
Honora pages 116, 122
Peter Wong Studio Collection page 137 left

Every effort has been made to trace copyright holders,
and the publishers will be happy to correct mistakes or
omissions in future editions.

contents

acknowledgments

Many people have been instrumental in the making of this book and I would like to start by thanking Dante Fasano, Lee Mandato, Joe Parcella, Toni Capelli, my agent, John White and his wife, Barbara, and of course my wife, Pam Spignesi whose support and love are two of the most important things in my life.

It always made sense to me that my book would be published by QVC whose presence in the jewelry industry continues to grow due to its quality and array of beautiful designs. Sarah Butterworth, Jill Cohen, and Cassandra Reynolds at QVC Publishing literally made this book happen. The many people in the jewelry department past and present at QVC who believed in this book and made it what it is, are testimony to the collaboration that can exist even in the largest of organizations. My thanks to Grace Giovanangelo, David Markstein, Cynthia Carlson, Anne Luttrell, Bernadette Turner, Sue Kelly, Dan Chase, Sue Atherholt, and Paul Callaro.

I would especially like to thank John Koivula, Tom Moses, and Dean Stevens for their valuable contributions.

Lastly the gorgeous photography from Carlos Alejandro with help from stylist Caroline Cotton and the beautiful design by Karen Salsgiver really give *Gems, Jewels, and Treasures* a sumptuous look— I really appreciate their talents.

Stephen Spignesi
New Haven, Connecticut

introduction

Looking back over my career as a gemologist working at the Gemological Institute of America (a nonprofit organization that was founded nearly seven decades ago with a mission to actively promote gemological research and education), I often think of it as my years spent "practicing" gemology. Each day has brought new challenges and insights and the years have given me a broad perspective on the myriad aspects of the gemstone business. I am always struck by the range of gemstone varieties used in today's jewelry designs and impressed by the development of clear industry-wide standards. I have recently noticed an emphasis in the jewelry industry on meeting the increasing demand for consumer education—providing people with the opportunity to increase their knowledge of gemstones and jewelry.

Consumer education has never been more important than it is today, as more and more varieties and uses of gemstones are available to the consumer and I am delighted to find in these pages basic information about gemstones and jewelry, presented in a practical and user-friendly manner. The book covers not only the timeless classics—such as gold, silver, diamonds, emeralds, and rubies— but also does a wonderful service of including less well known, but increasingly desirable, gemstones and jewelry.

I am especially pleased to see a section on gemstone treatment, which provides the reader with important information on the processes in use today to enhance gemstones, ensuring that customers have the information they need to make informed decisions about their jewelry purchases.

Along with descriptions of the gemstones, their sources, their relative rarity, and their most popular cuts and uses, the reader will find delightful accounts of the legends, lore, and powers associated with each stone. For all who enjoy and learn from this book, I extend my good wishes that they profit from its knowledge.

Tom Moses
Gemological Institute of America

most popular

g

gemstones

As in a cabinet or chest

One jewel may exceed the rest.

AN COLLINS,
Divine Songs and Meditacions

WHAT IS AGATE? *Agate is a variety of uniquely patterned chalcedony (a translucent form of quartz) known for its lovely bands of color. It is this marked color banding that distinguishes agate from other forms of chalcedony such as carnelian, jasper, and chrysoprase. There are many fascinating varieties of the gemstone, including the following:*

BANDED AGATE: *Displays distinctive and vivid stripes or bands.*

DENDRITIC AGATE: *Contains dark inclusions that look like tree branches, ferns, moss, or landscapes.*

FIRE AGATE: *Contains iridescent layers created through the diffraction and refraction of light at the inclusions within the gemstone. Mined in the United States in Arizona, California, and northern Mexico.*

LACE AGATE: *Displays beautiful lacelike circular patterns.*

PLUME AGATE: *A type of dendritic agate that looks like it has a beautiful array of feathers inside the stone.*

agate

Where is agate found?

One of the largest and most important sources for agate since the sixteenth century has been the Idar–Oberstein region of Germany, about seventy miles southwest of Frankfurt. Today, however, Uruguay and Brazil are the major suppliers of agate. Agate is also found in Italy, Egypt, Scotland, China, Mexico, and Madagascar. Moss agate comes from India, the United States, and China. (The Petrified Forest in Arizona is a major source of petrified wood. Petrified wood is fossilized wood in which the organic wood has been replaced by quartz or another mineral. Petrified wood is a fascinating hybrid of wood and gemstone, and many people collect it because of its beauty and unique nature.)

LEGEND AND LORE Persian magicians used agates to ward off storms, and agate has been used for healing since Babylonian times. Agate's reputed powers of protection are remarkable and wide-ranging. Agate is believed to protect the wearer from the evil eye as well as to ensure God's grace. Agate is also said to protect a person from lightning, shield its wearer from danger and bodily harm of all manner, impart courage, and prevent children from falling. Blue lace agate is credited with the power to break down stubbornness in a person, cure headaches, increase optimism and happiness, ease depression, and clear mental clutter. Moss agate is reputed to promote healing of wounds, relieve tension, and increase longevity; plume agate to enhance sexuality and stimulate creativity and focus. All banded agates are reputed to give the timid added confidence and provide the courage to fend off stress of all kinds. Legend also holds that agate can act as performance enhancers and improve problem-solving abilities. Agate is a lucky and supportive stone for actors, airline workers, artists, chefs, construction workers, dancers, dentists, educators, electricians, environmentalists, farmers, homemakers, police officers, postal workers, taxi drivers, and veterinarians.

COLOR Agate occurs in many wonderful colors, including white, gray, green, brown, red, and blue, and individual stones are often speckled with a blend of several colors. Blue lace agate is especially appealing with its fine, lacy pattern of colored lines. (Petrified wood usually occurs in red or brown shades, although it is rarely used for jewelry.)

SHAPE Each piece of agate is unique, and jewelry designers tend to allow the stone to dictate the form of the piece. Pendant, pin, ring, and earring mountings are often designed to accommodate the individual contours of a particular piece of agate. You will rarely see agate cut into traditional faceted shapes, such as a marquise or emerald cut. Agate is usually cut into cabochons, carved into cameos, or made into beads. Ancient uses of agate included using the stone to make vessels and cylinder seals, as well as jewelry.

APPEAL Agate, used in a wide variety of rings, brooches, and pendants, is plentiful and affordable. Common stones are usually not judged by jewelry standards: agate is not evaluated with the quality grades used for other gemstones; the quality of an individual agate stone is essentially determined by its uniqueness and its visual appeal. And that is the key to choosing agate (its appeal to you determines its quality, although most agate fans would agree that the stones with the more vivid colors are the prettiest.) Agate stones with intricate banding or embedded images, such as trees, moss, or leaves are considered by many to be very desirable. Agate is relatively tough. It ranks a high six and one-half to seven on the Mohs scale and is a durable gemstone. Interestingly, in addition to being used in jewelry, agate is also used for knife edges, mortars, and pestles.

WHAT IS ALEXANDRITE? *Alexandrite is a rare and unique, color-changing form of the mineral chrysoberyl that was reportedly discovered in Russia's Ural Mountains in 1830 on Czar Alexander II's twelfth birthday and named in his honor. The finest natural alexandrite exhibits a dramatic color change, from vivid green in natural sunlight, to a deep purplish-red under incandescent (artificial) light. Alexandrite's color changes are a function of the stone's ability to absorb the different types of light into distinctly different body colors. Alexandrite is the gemstone of children born on Friday, one of the birthstones for June, and the commemorative gemstone for the fifty-fifth wedding anniversary.*

alexandrite

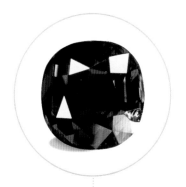

Where is alexandrite found?

· · · · · · ·

Alexandrite is found where it was first discovered, in the Ural Mountains of Russia, as well as in Brazil, East Africa, and Sri Lanka.

Alexandrite appears green in natural light and red in artificial light. The stone occurs in a wide range of intensity of each color, from pale grayish green to deep forest green, and from brownish-lavender to deep purple-red. Cat's-eye alexandrite is an exceptionally rare form of chrysoberyl, which not only exhibits the color-change phenomenon that characterizes alexandrite, but also shows a cat's-eye effect.

Alexandrite can be cut into all the faceted gemstone shapes: round brilliant, oval, pear, cushion, marquise, heart, square, trillion, fantasy, and emerald, which reveal the beauty and brilliance of the gemstone. Cat's eye alexandrite is cut into cabochons to exhibit the "eye".

The rarest most desirable alexandrite stones exhibit strong color-change and have no inclusions visible to the unaided eye.

LEGEND AND LORE Alexandrite is reputed to bring good luck, and to bring out the more refined and elegant characteristics of the wearer. Alexandrite worn on the left hand is said to provide protection from enemies. Some believe that alexandrite's green, "day" colors encourage happiness and success, and that its purple-red, "night" colors make the wearer warmer, more passionate, and more loving. Alexandrite reputedly can also make the wearer embrace life with passion and enthusiasm. Alexandrite is a lucky and supportive stone for dressmakers.

WHAT IS AMBER? *Amber, thought to be one of the earliest gemstones used by man, is a prehistoric tree resin that has fossilized. Some amber even has the fossilized remains of prehistoric organisms, like flies and other insects, trapped inside. Usually amber has a very appealing golden yellow or yellow-orange color. It has been a popular gemstone for adornment and jewelry since the time of the ancient Greeks and Romans. Amber beads and pendants have even been found in 750,000-year-old archeological sites.*

amber

Where is amber found?

The largest deposits of amber found to date are along the Baltic Sea coasts of nations such as Poland, Latvia, and Estonia. Other sources are Myanmar — where it is known as burmite, from the country's former name of Burma — and the Dominican Republic, Sicily, and in the United States, Mexico, Germany, Czechoslovakia, and Canada.

LEGEND AND LORE Throughout history, amber has been employed for a wide range of medicinal cures. The ancient Romans used it to treat goiters. Amber is believed to act as a remedy for many other ailments, including stomach problems, headaches, toothaches, breathing problems, and infections. Amber is also reputed to enhance mental clarity and allow the wearer to make decisions from a rational perspective rather than an emotional one. Amber can also allegedly lift the spirits and clarify a wearer's understanding of the past. Amber is the astrological stone for the sign of Leo and signifies a warm and sensitive nature, as well as a love of nature and all living things. Amber's yellow color is believed to enhance communication and honesty. Orange amber is said to motivate the wearer and promote strong organizational habits. Red amber is thought to exert a calming effect and may also help the wearer step back from emotional overreaction, promoting more logical thinking.

COLOR Amber is almost always yellow or golden yellow, although black and red amber have also been discovered. The popular yellow and golden varieties are the ones most often used for jewelry. (Clear amber was treasured as a material for rosary beads during the Middle Ages.)

SHAPE Amber is very soft and can be cut and polished into a variety of shapes, the most common being beads and cabochons. Amber is sometimes polished flat for setting in rings, pins, earrings, and pendants. One of the unique properties of amber is its lightness; a large necklace of amber beads or large amber earrings are surprisingly light.

APPEAL The overall visual appeal of surface and color, as well as the presence of inclusions, determines the desirability of individual stones. Amber is an organic substance and must be treated with care.

WHAT IS AMETHYST? *Amethyst is a purple form of transparent quartz crystal. Amethyst is the February birthstone and the gemstone of people born under the astrological sign of Pisces. It is also used as the commemorative gemstone for the sixth wedding anniversary.*

amethyst

Where is amethyst found?
· · · · · · · ·

Much of the world's amethyst is mined in Brazil, Uruguay, Bolivia, and Zambia. Brazilian amethyst is famous for its rich color and consistent clarity. African amethyst is noted for its color of royal purple with red undertones. Amethyst is also mined in the Ural Mountains of Russia, some of this amethyst may show a flash of red. It is also found in the United States, India, Germany, Madagascar, Australia, Mexico, and Canada; Canadian amethyst may have blue undertones.

Amethyst occurs in a complete range of the color purple, from soft lavender and lilac to a vivid purple or reddish-purple.

Amethysts are cut into all the faceted gemstone shapes: round brilliant, oval, pear, marquise, emerald, heart, square, trillion, and fantasy. Amethysts are also cut into cabochons, and fashioned into beads of various shapes. Popular uses for amethysts include rings, earrings, pendants, and brooches.

As with many transparent gemstones, the appeal of an individual amethyst stone is determined by both the intensity of its color and the number and size of its inclusions. The rarest amethysts are deeply and evenly colored, with few or no internal flaws. The more readily available amethysts are soft lavender in color and may contain inclusions; some may be visible to the naked eye, but they rarely detract from the glorious beauty of an amethyst.

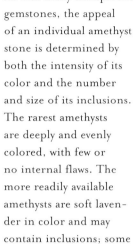

LEGEND AND LORE Legend has it that amethyst was created by Bacchus, the god of wine. One day Bacchus got so fed up with mortals that he swore that he would feed the next human to cross his path to the tigers. This unfortunate mortal happened to be a maiden named Amethyst, who unwittingly crossed Bacchus's path on her way to worship the goddess Diana. Diana outsmarted Bacchus, however, and changed Amethyst into a pillar of colorless quartz to save her from the tigers. Bacchus was so amazed by Diana's miracle that he poured his wine over Amethyst, changing her color to purple thus, the gemstone amethyst was created. This legend gave rise to the belief that wearing amethyst would protect one from drunkenness and poisoning, and would assure sober judgment. (The Greek word "amethyst" means "not drunk.") In addition, amethyst worn by a person born under the sign of Pisces is said to protect the wearer from making ill-advised decisions based on emotion, and to assist the Pisces-born in attaining fame in the arts. In Christian theology, amethyst has long been considered a symbol of the authority of the church. Amethyst is a lucky and supportive stone for artists and ministers.

WHAT IS AQUAMARINE? *Aquamarine is a beautiful, transparent blue form of the mineral beryl. It is the March birthstone and is also used as the commemorative gemstone for the nineteenth wedding anniversary. It is also the gemstone for the astrological sign of Taurus.*

aquamarine

Where is aquamarine found?
. . . .

A great deal of the world's finest aquamarine is found in Brazil. Aquamarine is also mined in Madagascar, the Ural Mountains in Russia, India, Italy, the Ukraine, China, Zambia, Pakistan, Afghanistan, Nigeria, and in the United States. China has become a newer source for a very attractive aquamarine that is being used in a complete range of jewelry styles.

The word aquamarine is derived from the Latin words *aqua marina*, which mean "sea water." Aquamarine is available in a lovely range of blue, from a blue so pale as to appear almost colorless, to deeper sky blues and blue-greens. Nigerian aquamarine is known for its intense color, whereas a milky, blue aquamarine is available from many sources.

The rarest of the aquamarines are medium blue with few and minor inclusions (flaws). Because of the transparent nature of aquamarine, larger flaws will be visible. The good news is that stones with few flaws are available.

Aquamarine can be cut into all the faceted gemstone shapes: round brilliant, oval, pear, marquise, heart, cushion, square, trillion, fantasy, and emerald. It is also cut into cabochons. You will also find aquamarine shaped into beads.

LEGEND AND LORE According to legend, aquamarine has medicinal powers, as demonstrated by an old belief that drinking water in which an aquamarine has been soaked will cure hiccups. The ancients also believed aquamarine could cure ailments of the jaw, throat, liver, and stomach, as well as relieve toothaches. Ancient Roman physicians used aquamarine to improve digestion and to lessen fluid retention. It is believed that aquamarine can surround the wearer with an aura that others subconsciously read as an air of insightful authority. Because of its intrinsic connection with the sea, some believe that wearing aquamarine can exert a calming effect, similar to the calm one feels around bodies of water. The Roman philosopher Pliny the Elder described aquamarines "of a sea green color, the color of the sea when it is calm." The stone has long been a talisman of good luck for sailors. If you dream of an aquamarine, legend has it that you will soon experience new happiness and make new friends. Aquamarine is also said to improve eyesight, stimulate the intellect, and is reputed to help save troubled marriages. Not surprisingly, aquamarine is a lucky and supportive stone for divers.

WHAT IS CAT'S-EYE? *Cat's-eye is a hard, honey yellow form of chrysoberyl that shows a white or nearly white line down its length when the stone is properly cut into a cabochon shape. Genuine cat's-eye is not the same as tiger's-eye quartz or quartz cat's-eye, which are more common, less expensive quartz stones that have a similar "eye" effect when cut into cabochons. (See Tiger's-Eye Quartz page 56.) Strictly speaking, cat's-eye chrysoberyl and cat's-eye alexandrite chrysoberyl are the only two gemstones that can properly be called simply cat's-eye—without including the mineral name. Cat's-eye commemorates the eighteenth wedding anniversary.*

cat's-eye

Where is cat's-eye found?
. . . .

Cat's-eye is found primarily in Sri Lanka and Brazil, although it is also found in Africa and in the Ural Mountains of Russia.

The cat's-eye variety of chrysoberyl occurs in the range of honey yellow to honey brown, and greenish-yellow to yellowish-green.

In order to appreciate fully the "eye" effect of cat's-eye, the stones are cut into cabochons. Chrysoberyl in its other forms—alexandrite in particular—is cut into the faceted shapes, but cat's-eye chrysoberyl is cut en cabochon.

The rarest cat's-eye stones have some very unique and distinctive characteristics: the "eye" band is straight, has sharp edges, is not too wide, extends the entire length of the stone, and is positioned in the center of the stone. This band should be a lovely white or gray color, a distinctly different color than the body color of the stone itself.

LEGEND AND LORE Not surprisingly, cat's-eye is reputed to ward off the "evil eye." The ancient Assyrians believed that wearing a cat's-eye stone could make the wearer invisible. The ancients also feared people who wore a cat's-eye because they believed that these people could see through walls and closed doors. In all its forms, cat's-eye is said to promote healing. Legend holds that cat's-eye is a powerful beauty aid that promotes youthfulness in the wearer. Cat's-eye is also said to guard a person's wealth and to even restore wealth lost prior to owning the stone. Cat's-eye is believed to guard mental health, alleviate depression, and enhance joy. It is said to aid in decision-making by promoting clear thinking. Cat's-eye is a lucky and supportive stone for all those who work in the creative arts; it is also a good luck talisman for gamblers.

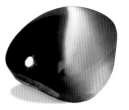

WHAT IS CITRINE? *Citrine is the yellow variety of quartz. Citrine is sometimes used as an alternate November birthstone, although golden topaz is the traditional birthstone for the month. Citrine is also the commemorative gemstone for the thirteenth wedding anniversary.*

citrine

Where is citrine found?
• • • • • • •

Citrine is available from Brazil (Rio Grande citrine and Madeira citrine), Madagascar, Russia, Uruguay, Hungary, the United States, and Colombia (Palmyra citrine).

LEGEND AND LORE The name citrine comes from the French word *citron,* which means "lemon" and the Latin word *citrus,* which means "citron tree." Citrine is the gemstone for people born under the astrological sign of Scorpio and it has long been associated with lightheartedness, cheerfulness, and hope; it is also a symbol of the mind and intellect. Citrine is reputed to have wondrous medicinal properties, including the power to guard against shortness of breath, aid the digestive system, cleanse the body of toxins, and assure a clear complexion. Citrine is a guardian stone, too, allegedly able to protect the wearer against libel, evil thoughts, alcoholism, and even snake bites. Citrine has long been believed capable of calming and soothing its wearers, even to the point of curing depression. Many also believe that citrine can stimulate effective communication and increase personal productivity, as well as assure a good night's sleep and prevent nightmares. Citrine is a lucky and supportive stone for salespeople, radio and TV workers, recreational workers, and singers.

COLOR Citrine occurs in yellow, golden yellow, orange, and orange-brown. The majority of stones are an intense golden yellow. The reddish-orange color is not abundant; this variety of citrine is known as Madeira citrine because its color resembles the color of Madeira wine.

SHAPE Citrine can be cut into all the faceted gemstone shapes: round brilliant, oval, pear, marquise, heart, cushion, square, trillion, fantasy, and emerald. It is also cut into cabochons and beads.

APPEAL The most well known citrine color is an intense golden yellow. Many consumers are opting more for the brighter yellow stones, which go so beautifully with the colors of contemporary fashion. Citrine is very popular for use in rings, pendants, and earrings, which are especially stunning on women with dark hair or when worn with black or dark brown clothing. As with most transparent gemstones, an absence of inclusions generally signifies a higher quality stone.

WHAT IS CORAL? *Coral is an organic substance that is actually the skeleton of a small marine animal called a coral polyp. These creatures live in branching colonies that form coral reefs and atolls, as the lower levels of the animals die and the newer generations grow on top of them.*

coral

Where is coral found?
. . . .

Coral is found in warm waters off the coast of Japan, and also in the Red Sea, and along the Mediterranean, African, and Malaysian coasts. Black coral is found in the waters around the West Indies, Australia, and along the coast of many of the Pacific islands. A black coral known as King's Coral has been fished off the Cameroon Coast.

LEGEND AND LORE The word coral comes from the Greek word *Koraillion* and it has long been associated with the ocean and the element of water. The Ancient Greeks believed that after Perseus decapitated Medusa, he threw her head into the trees lining the shore, whereupon their branches turned into stone. When the sea nymphs took these branches into the water, they became the seeds for coral reefs along the Mediterranean Coast. Italian women wear coral to regulate their menses and believe that coral earrings can attract the affection of men. Red coral is worn by newlyweds to assure fertility and guarantee children. According to legend, if you touch a piece of coral to the doors and windows of your house, your home will attract good luck for all who live there. Coral is said to guard against accidents and acts of violence, and to protect sailors and guard against shipwreck and shark attacks. Coral is given to a child to assure health and well-being as the child grows, and some believe that rubbing coral on the gums of children who are teething helps relieve their pain. Coral's reputed powers are significant: it can guard against the evil eye and demons, as well as relieve indigestion, stop bleeding, and cure diseases of the eye. In some countries, coral is placed on graves to guard the souls of the deceased. Coral is also believed to create an emotional openness in its wearer and to generate excitement and enthusiasm. Coral is a lucky and supportive gemstone for singers.

COLOR Coral comes in lovely shades of red and pink—the most popular hues. It also occurs in the colors of white, black, blue, orange, and gold. Japanese coral is almost always red, pink, or white.

SHAPE Coral is hand-carved into jewelry and figurines, cut and polished into cabochons, and fashioned into beads for stringing. Oval cabochons are a very popular cut for coral rings, pendants, and earrings.

APPEAL A vivid red color and a smooth luster are marks of a quality coral piece, although deep red coral is rare. Black coral is always highly polished. White coral with a tinge of pink—known as angel-skin coral—is very attractive. As with all gemstones including pearl, amber, ivory, shell, as well as coral, the beauty of a piece is in the eye of the beholder. Many people delight in the natural "woodgrain" lines found in individual pieces of coral.

WHAT IS CHROME DIOPSIDE? *Chrome diopside is a transparent mineral that has a strikingly attractive green color. The very bright green form of this gemstone is often referred to as chrome diopside because its vivid color results from the presence of chromium in the mineral.*

chrome diopside

Where is diopside found?
· · · · · · ·

Most chrome diopside is found today in Siberia in Russia (Russian green diopside), as well as in South Africa, Pakistan, Austria, Brazil, the United States, Canada, Sri Lanka, and Madagascar.

COLOR

The color of chrome diopside is an exceptionally vivid green. The most brightly colored chrome diopside stones are usually two carats or less; larger stones tend to look darker and lose their vivid green color. For someone wanting a stunning green stone, chrome diopside is a beautiful alternative to more expensive emeralds.

APPEAL

As with other transparent gemstones, the quality of chrome diopside is determined by the depth and uniformity of color and the presence or absence of internal inclusions and external blemishes. Chrome diopside's vivid green color, coupled with its affordability, has increased its popularity as a jewelry stone.

SHAPE

Chrome diopside is cut into all the faceted gemstone shapes: round brilliant, oval, pear, marquise, emerald, heart, square, trillion, and fantasy. Chrome diopside is also cut into cabochons and occasionally fashioned into beads of various shapes.

LEGEND AND LORE Chrome diopside is reputed to be a fever reducer. It can supposedly balance your body temperature and even alleviate aches and pains caused by fever. Recently, Russia has elevated its chrome diopside to the elite realm of class-one exports, making it one of only four gemstones granted this status. The other three are diamond, emerald, and alexandrite.

WHAT IS EMERALD? *Emerald is a green, transparent form of the mineral beryl; in fact, emerald is the most precious type of beryl. Emerald is one of the trinity of most valued and treasured colored gemstones; the other two are ruby and sapphire. Emerald is the May birthstone and is used as the commemorative gemstone for the twentieth and thirty-fifth wedding anniversaries.*

emerald

Where is emerald found?
. . . .

Fine emeralds are found in Colombia, Brazil, South Africa, Zambia, Zimbabwe, Pakistan, Afghanistan, Russia, India, Norway, Australia, and North Carolina in the United States. Historically, the earliest emerald mines were Cleopatra's, by The Red Sea of Upper Egypt.

LEGEND AND LORE Emeralds take their name from the Persian word for green, and the gemstone has long been thought to bless its wearer with eternal love. In ancient times, gem lovers were enchanted by the emerald's inner radiance and often compared it to the "captured glow of the firefly", and the ancient Greeks dedicated the stone to Venus, the goddess of love. Emeralds are also believed to have medicinal properties, including the ability to improve liver function, cure back pain and stomach troubles, and lessen the effects of diabetes. Julius Caesar wore emeralds and believed they warded off eye disease and epilepsy. In addition to improving vision, emeralds are said to provide resistance to poisons and to protect the wearer from witchcraft. The ancient Romans believed that emeralds eased stress and cured depression. Emeralds, as a natural tranquilizer, are believed to shorten labor and hasten childbirth when a stone is placed on the thigh of a woman in labor. Emeralds are also said to promote honesty in the wearer, as well as to protect wearers from accidents of all kinds. Sailors have traditionally had faith that emeralds protect them on the open sea. Emeralds have long symbolized the season of spring, rebirth, and hope. Emerald is a lucky and supportive stone for environmentalists, doctors, and nurses.

COLOR Emeralds occur in specific shades of green, from a green to a deep, velvety bluish green. Beryl stones of different hues of green that lack the chemistry and the characteristic emerald color are considered green beryl and not emerald.

SHAPE Emerald is cut into all the faceted gemstone shapes: round brilliant, oval, pear, marquise, emerald, heart, square, trillion, and fantasy. Emerald is also cut into cabochons and fashioned into beads of various shapes. Historically, emeralds were also carved into cameos, intaglios, and figurines.

APPEAL As in all transparent stones, the rarest emeralds are intensely colored and have few inclusions (flaws). Large emeralds of this quality are exceptionally rare, and consequently the most expensive. A few extraordinary emeralds exist that are so large, so deeply green, and so internally clean that they have not even been set into jewelry and worn. These are exceptions, but the desirability of all emeralds increases as the color becomes more vivid and inclusions become less visible. It should be noted, however, that emeralds stand alone when it comes to inclusions. Jewelers will accept inclusions in an emerald that would be unacceptable in any other gemstone. Some inclusions are acceptable due to the rarity of emeralds, their growth environment, and recovery methods.

WHAT IS GARNET? *Garnet is the umbrella term used to name a number of colored, transparent gemstones occurring in all colors except blue. The red varieties of garnet are most commonly used as the January birthstone; rhodolite garnet (red-purple) is used as the commemorative gemstone for the second wedding anniversary; Tsavorite garnet (green) is often used for the twelfth wedding anniversary.*

garnet

Where is garnet found?
. . . .

Garnet is found in many places around the globe. Important sources include five bountiful mines in Kenya (Tsavorite garnet is named after Kenya's Tsavo National Park). It is also found in Afghanistan, Australia, Brazil and several other South American countries, Canada, Germany, Hungary, India, Israel, Italy, Kenya, Madagascar, Mexico, Myanmar, Namibia, Russia, Siberia, Sri Lanka, Sweden, Tanzania, and the United States, especially Arizona, California, Maine, New Hampshire, and Virginia.

Popular varieties of garnet include the following colors.
Red: Pyrope (red, pinkish-red), almandine (red, brownish-red, purplish-red), rhodolite (pink, purplish-pink, reddish-purple).

Green: Demantoid andradite (transparent yellow-green, light to dark green), tsavorite (shades of green and often called the Rolls-Royce of green gemstones).

Orange/Yellow: Grossularite (fiery orangish-red, canary yellow, green, colorless), hessonite (a brown to orange-brown to yellow, orange and red-orange variety of grossularite), spessartite (orange, orangish-brown, tangerine, yellow, yellow-brown), mandarin (orange), malaia (orange, pinkish-orange, peach). *Color changing or shifting:* A few garnets change, or shift, color when seen under different kinds of light.

Blue: recently, a few blue garnets have been discovered in East Africa.

Garnet is cut into all the faceted gemstone shapes: round brilliant, oval, pear, marquise, emerald, heart, square, trillion, and fantasy. Garnet is also cut into rose cuts, cabochons, and fashioned into beads of various shapes.

Garnet is a plentiful, affordable gemstone. Clean stones are readily available, so most evaluations of quality focus on the depth, intensity, and uniformity of a particular garnet's body color. The vividness of the range of colors exhibited in the different varieties of garnet make them suitable for use in all kinds of jewelry, and the right color is always available for different complexions and different colored clothing.

LEGEND AND LORE Garnet has long symbolized fire, faith, and loyalty. Legend tells us that Noah hung a garnet on the ark. In Christian symbolism the blood-red garnet represents the blood Jesus shed on the Cross. Garnet is said to lighten heaviness of the heart, relieve depression, and encourage loyalty and devotion in the wearer. Garnet also has reputed medicinal properties, including the ability to prevent skin diseases, stop bleeding, cure inflammatory diseases like arthritis and rheumatism, and rid the body of toxins. Red garnet is said to cure fevers, and yellow garnet to cure jaundice. In the thirteenth century, garnet was used as an insect repellent, and powdered garnet was once used as a poison antidote. Garnet can also allegedly stimulate the heart and encourage productivity and success in business—especially for women. The almandine variety of garnet is believed to discourage laziness and encourage purposeful focus in the wearer. Dreaming of garnet symbolizes enormous wealth—garnets are lucky stones—and the possibility that a mystery will soon be solved.

WHAT IS HEMATITE? *Hematite is a blackish, metallic mineral. Hematite is very dense and heavy; it is both carved into figurines and used as jewelry.*

hematite

Where is hematite found?
. . . .

Hematite is found in solidified molten rocks around Lake Superior (both the United States and Canadian sides), in Quebec in Canada, in Brazil, Venezuela, England, Germany, Norway, Sweden, and on the Italian island of Elba in the Mediterranean.

Hematite is almost always black to very dark gray. A less dense form of this mineral is reddish, but it is not used in jewelry.

Hematite may be cut into the faceted gemstone shapes, but its most popular use is as beads. It may also be cut and polished into cabochons or carved into cameos and intaglios.

The metallic luster of its surface is unique to hematite. The quality of hematite itself is very consistent: all you need to look for to evaluate a piece is the quality of the shaping, carving, and finish.

LEGEND AND LORE Hematite's folk name is "volcano spit" and in Italy hematite necklaces are sold under that name. Hematite's legendary powers begin with its ability to actually heal itself: if you scratch the surface of a hematite stone and then rub your finger over the scratch, the line may vanish. Not surprisingly, hematite is believed to be able to draw illness from the body. It is also believed to calm and center the emotions and to guide priests in carrying out their pastoral duties. According to legend, hematite makes its wearer alert and charmingly personable, and can also bring about a successful resolution to litigation. Hematite is also reputed to stimulate the libido. Some psychics also believe that hematite provides a key to understanding past lives.

WHAT IS JADE? *Jade is a word that actually describes two specific minerals, jadeite and nephrite. In 1863, the French chemist Augustine Damour identified these two types of jade, although the differences between jadeite and nephrite had been known to the Chinese since the mid-eighteenth century. Jadeite is the rarer of the two varieties of the gemstone, as well as being the harder of the two. The finest jadeite is called Imperial jade. Jadeite is the jade most often used for jewelry today. Nephrite is not as hard as jadeite, but ironically, its interlocking crystalline structure makes it a little stronger. It was even used for weapons, such as daggers and clubs, in ancient times.*

jade

Where is jade found?

· · · · · · ·

The finest jadeite comes from Myanmar. Jadeite is also found in Russia, Japan, Guatemala, and California in the United States. Nephrite is found in China, Taiwan, New Zealand, Switzerland, Brazil, British Columbia, Poland, Germany, India, Canada, Mexico, and in Alaska, California, and Wyoming in the United States. Dark green nephrite is found in Siberia, Canada, and in Zimbabwe; black nephrite is found in Australia.

When Spanish conquistadors invaded Mexico in the sixteenth century, they discovered that the natives were wearing jade to cure kidney problems, so the conquistadors called the beautiful stone *piedra de ijada,* which means "stone of the loins." Interestingly, the ancient Romans also believed that jade was a cure for inflammation of the kidneys or "nephritis", and called the stone *lapis nephriticus,* which eventually was shortened and Anglicized to nephrite. Jade's wide range of colors has long been associated with the bounties of nature, and many believe that the stone can affect the weather. Jade, considered a gift from God, has had various mystical and spiritual properties attributed to it, including the power to enhance inner purity, higher consciousness, intellectual superiority, musical talent, and the virtue of loyalty. It also represents good fortune and abounding health. Jade is reputed to stimulate optimism and promote understanding of the opposite sex. White jade is believed to cure intestinal trouble, while black jade is said to imbue the wearer with strength. Jade is a lucky and supportive stone for doctors and nurses, educators, and military personnel.

COLOR Jadeite occurs in a wide range of colors, including a complete range of green and speckled green, lavender, brownish-orange, honey yellow, white, black, and gray. Nephrite is mostly green, with gray, black, or brown undertones. Nephrite also occurs in completely gray or black varieties, as well as a grayish white form sometimes referred to as "mutton-fat" jade and especially favored for carving figurines.

SHAPE Both forms of jade are cut and polished into beads, cut into cabochons, and carved into cameos, intaglios, and figurines. Jade is occasionally cut into the faceted gemstone shapes, although the cabochon is the more popular and traditional style for the stone.

APPEAL The appeal of both types of jade is due to jade's lovely colors as well as its texture and its semitransparent or translucent quality. In fine jade pieces, light seems to enter the stone instead of stopping flatly at the surface.

WHAT IS LAPIS LAZULI? *Lapis lazuli or lapis is a truly gorgeous opaque blue stone with white or golden flecks. It is composed of several minerals, including lazurite, calcite, pyrite, and sodalite. Its vivid blue color makes lapis lazuli a most distinctive gemstone. Lapis lazuli's name comes from two sources: the Latin word for stone,* **lapis,** *and the Persian word for blue,* **lazhward.** *It is an alternate birthstone for December, and it is the commemorative gemstone for the ninth wedding anniversary.*

lapis lazuli

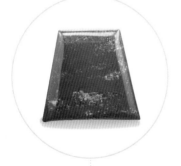

Where is lapis lazuli found?
. . . .

The world's finest lapis lazuli is found in northeastern Afghanistan, where it has been mined for over five thousand years. Lapis lazuli is plentiful in Chile and Argentina, and is also found in Turkistan, Russia, the United States, and Canada.

LEGEND AND LORE Ancient alchemists called lapis lazuli the "Stone of Heaven." Tradition holds that the Ten Commandments given to Moses were engraved on lapis tablets. Ancient Egyptians believed that lapis cured depression and that it also provided comfort to the dead on their journey to the next world. Accordingly, they decorated the inside of tombs with lapis to assist the deceased into the afterlife. Ancient Macedonians used charms made of lapis to prevent miscarriages, and ground lapis was used to make a salve to reduce inflammation of the eyes. Lapis has long been thought to be a protection against the evil eye, especially when the stone is cut into the shape of an eye. Lapis is also said to balance the emotions and allow a detached assessment of an emotionally charged situation. Wearers of lapis are believed to be especially watched over by God and destined for great success. Lapis is said to bestow strength upon the wearer, sensitivity, and self-confidence, and legend holds that a timid child will become courageous by wearing a necklace made of lapis. Lapis lazuli is a lucky and supportive stone of archaeologists, historians, executives, inventors, journalists, lawyers, psychologists, and writers.

COLOR Lapis lazuli occurs naturally in a range of blues; the darker and more intense colors have traditionally been the more desired. Lapis will often have specks of calcite, which gives it its characteristic white flecks, or pyrite, which results in the gold flecks. A modern type of lapis, denim lapis, is a lighter blue overall because of its greater concentration of calcite, which creates white patterns throughout the stones.

SHAPE Lapis is cut into cabochons, cut and polished into beads, and carved into figurines. Recently, lapis lazuli has been cut into faceted shapes that look very attractive when set in sterling silver.

APPEAL The overall appeal of an individual piece of lapis lies in the vividness of the stone's blue color combined with its intriguing white and gold specks. All types of lapis lazuli are quite striking and color choice is a matter of individual preference.

WHAT IS MALACHITE? *Malachite is a stunning opaque green mineral made of copper carbonate. It is known for its distinctive bands of black and different shades of green, which are similar to the color banding found in agate.*

malachite

Where is malachite found?
· · · · · · ·

Malachite is most plentiful in the Congo, although it is also found in Russia, Zambia, and in New Mexico and Arizona in the United States.

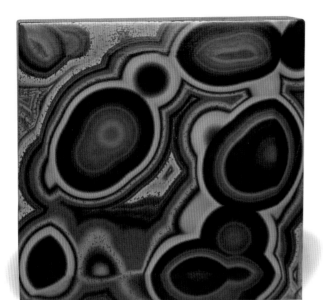

Malachite occurs in a vivid kelly green with alternating light and dark green bands, interspersed with black bands.

Malachite is cut into cabochons for pins, earrings, and pendants; it is also cut and polished into beads. Malachite makes an excellent carving medium for figurines and boxes, and is also ground and used as a pigment in fine-arts paints.

Like other opaque stones, the quality of a malachite stone is judged by the intensity of its color and smoothness of its surface. The most appealing malachites are vivid green stones with distinct color banding and a smooth, flawless surface. Malachite is plentiful and affordable; exceptionally beautiful and high-quality malachite stones can be found in a wide range of sizes and shapes.

LEGEND AND LORE The name malachite comes from the Greek word *molochites,* which refers to the herb mallow. Legend holds that malachite can enhance visionary powers, promote inner peace, and defend the wearer against negativity of all kinds. Malachite is reputed to cure circulatory disorders and to protect the wearer from physical dangers. Malachite is also known as the "salesman's stone" because it is believed to have the power to improve relationships with business associates. According to legend, a small piece of malachite placed in the drawer of a cash register can actually attract customers. A malachite worn by a child allegedly will protect against bad dreams, and malachite worn against the skin will open up one's heart and enhance the power to give and receive love. Malachite can also be used as a meditation tool and a sleep aid: staring at a piece of the soothing green stone is believed to relax the mind and ease depression, and if a piece of malachite jewelry is worn to bed, it will assure sound sleep. Malachite is a lucky and supportive gemstone for pilots, airline workers, miners, and secretaries.

WHAT IS ONYX? *Onyx is a variety of the quartz mineral chalcedony. Onyx may be anything from semitranslucent to completely opaque. Black onyx is one of the commemorative gemstones for the seventh wedding anniversary.*

onyx

Where is onyx found?
· · · · · · ·

Onyx is found throughout the world, including the United States. Large amounts of chalcedony are found in Uruguay and Brazil.

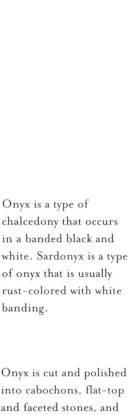

LEGEND AND LORE Onyx, as a type of
chalcedony, is believed to protect ocean voyagers
from storms at sea and to drive away evil spirits.
Ancient peoples wore chalcedony of all kinds
to protect their mental health and to fend off
depression. Reputedly, onyx can also bring its
wearer strength and assure victory in battle —
all while bestowing the wearer with a pleasant
disposition. Onyx is also said to reduce fevers,
cure insomnia, and make the wearer careful
and cautious in all things. According to legend,
onyx can not only relieve pain when placed on
the bellies of women in labor, but it can also
assist the new mothers later with their nursing.
Onyx is also reputed to balance the female
energies present in both sexes; the darker stones
are said to enhance the power and energies of
men, whereas the lighter, "gentler" stones are
believed to especially empower women.

COLOR Onyx is a type of
chalcedony that occurs
in a banded black and
white. Sardonyx is a type
of onyx that is usually
rust-colored with white
banding.

SHAPE Onyx is cut and polished
into cabochons, flat-top
and faceted stones, and
beads of all shapes; it is
also carved into cameos
and intaglios. Onyx's
striking color and smooth
texture make it an espe-
cially appealing medium
for carvings and figurines;
one of the most distinctive
uses of carved onyx is for
chess pieces.

APPEAL Onyx is plentiful and
affordable, and its
appeal is based on its
color and the smooth-
ness of its surface. All
black onyx is considered
of equal quality, as long
as the color is uniform
and the cutting of the
stone is attractive; the
value of black onyx is
related to the size of the
stone and the craftsman-
ship of its cut.

WHAT IS OPAL? *Opal is a translucent gemstone that boasts a beautiful, play-of-color. It occurs in a wide rainbow of colors, as well as white and black.*
The deeply colored stones with an intense fire of many colors are the rarest and most valuable opals. Different types of opal include milk (white), fire (yellow and red), black, and Brazilian (a milk opal with a blue-green play-of-color). Sections of opal are also used with other natural minerals or even man-made materials to make doublets, triplets, and mosaics (see Color*). Opal is the October birthstone and is the commemorative gemstone for the fourteenth wedding anniversary.*

opal

Where is opal found?
. . . .

The main sources for opal today are Australia and Mexico; it is also found in Oregon, Nevada, and elsewhere in the United States. Opals are also mined in Czechoslovakia, South Africa, and Brazil. Black opal was discovered in Australia in 1903.

Opals occur naturally in a wide range of varieties and colors; the different types of natural opals are:

Milk opal: refers to a group of opals with a white body color and a play-of-color that ranges from very subtle to brilliant. Included in the milk opals are white opals, gray opals, crystal opals, Brazilian opals, and jelly opals.

Fire opals: have red, orange, or yellow body colors and may exhibit either little or no play-of-color, or very intense and lively play-of-color. Mexico is the main source for fire opals. Fire opals are often labeled by the predominance of their body color, as in red opal and yellow opal.

Black opal: refers to a group of opals characterized by stunning and distinct play-of-color against a dark or black body color. Black opal is considered one of the better grades of opal and often commands a high per-carat price.

Opal Doublet: is a thin layer of opal cemented to a flat, often black stone such as onyx. The resulting doublet mimics the more expensive black opal and can be quite beautiful.

Opal Triplet: an opal doublet to which a protective top layer of colorless quartz, or even glass, has been added enhance the colors of the opal layer below.

Opal Mosaic: an arrangement of many small, irregularly shaped, multicolored pieces of opal that are cemented into lovely patterns and set in rings and pendants.

Opals are cut into round, marquise, pear, oval, or heart-shaped cabochons, and into shapes with a flat top. Fire opals that are all one color are sometimes faceted. In some special instances, in order to preserve an individual opal's unique play-of-color, a pendant, brooch, earring, or ring mounting will be designed to accommodate the natural shape of the stone rather than cutting the stone to fit a standard mounting.

The appeal of an individual opal is determined by the intensity of its fire, in other words, the beauty and uniqueness of its play-of-color. In general, pale, single-color, opaque opals are somewhat less popular than translucent, vividly colored stones. The rarest stones have deep, very intense play-of-color and fire, and boast many gorgeous colors. Other desirable opals are strikingly beautiful, have strong fire, and often show several colors; these usually have a white or a clear body color. More available opals have medium fire and a few distinct colors; they also usually have a white or clear body color. Some stones, usually whitish, have almost no play-of-color; these opals are often used in less expensive jewelry.

LEGEND AND LORE Opals are a symbol of hope, fidelity, and purity; for centuries, opals have been associated with spirituality and prayer. The name opal comes from the Sanskrit word *upala,* which means "precious stone." Caesar Augustus once wanted to sell a third of the Roman Empire for one opal. The many colors of opal are believed to represent the many faces of Eve, the first woman. Opal is also known as the "Cupid stone" because it is believed that opals have the power to attract romance and love, and to enhance a person's inner beauty. In ancient times, opals were wrapped in bay leaves and carried in an attempt to make the bearer invisible. During the Crusades, a wife would give her husband an opal to carry with him as protection in battle. An opal placed on the belly of a woman in labor is reputed to ease the pain of childbirth. Opal is said to enhance a person's natural, but buried, psychic powers, and opals are believed to facilitate a person's access to past lives. Opals are also said to bring good luck and attract money. Opal is a lucky and supportive gemstone for dancers and musicians.

WHAT IS PERIDOT? *Peridot is the green transparent gemstone variety of the mineral olivine. It has a distinctive yellow-green to yellowish-green color. Peridot is the August birthstone and is the commemorative gemstone for the sixteenth wedding anniversary.*

peridot

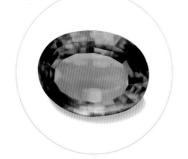

Where is peridot found?
. . . .

Peridot is mined in China, Pakistan, Myanmar, Norway, South Africa, Australia, Brazil, and in Arizona and Hawaii in the United States. Peridot is also found on the island of Zabargad in the Red Sea, which has been an abundant source for the gemstone since 1500 A.D.

The name peridot comes from a French word that was probably derived from the Arabic word *faridat,* which means "gem." Egyptian pharaohs wore the finest peridots; Egyptian priests wore less beautiful peridots, which in any case were supposed to eliminate the jealousy and envy that the pharaohs might have felt toward the priests. In ancient Roman times, peridot was worn to relieve depression. It has long been believed that peridot can eliminate negativity and pessimism, relieve anxiety and fear, and quell intense anger. Peridot is also a healing stone and is believed to be able to cure muscular problems, aid in alleviating liver disorders, and promote healing of insect bites. Peridot is also said to have the power to enhance friendships and lift the spirits, as well as to break a person out of a rut. Peridot is said to have the power to act as a sleep aid if worn to bed and also guards against spells, night terrors, hallucinations, and the evil eye.

COLOR Peridot occurs in shades of yellow-green to yellowish-green, including olive green.

SHAPE Peridot can be cut into all the faceted gemstone shapes: round brilliant, oval, pear, marquise, heart, cushion, square, trillion, fantasy, and emerald. It is also cut into cabochons and beads.

APPEAL Peridot's popularity is due to the uniqueness of its color and its beautiful transparency. Peridot set in yellow gold makes a striking and dramatic piece of jewelry, and its delicate color complements many complexions and fashion colors.

WHAT IS QUARTZ? *Quartz, which humans have known of for centuries, is a versatile mineral that occurs in colorless, translucent, transparent, and colored varieties. A wide range of popular gemstones are quartz, including agate, amethyst, ametrine, chrysoprase, citrine, cat's-eye quartz, onyx, and tiger's-eye quartz — several of which have their own chapters in this book. Stones that are marketed specifically as quartz include black quartz, Ginger® quartz, Límon® quartz, rose quartz, and smoky quartz.*

quartz

Where is quartz found?
. . . .

Quartz is found in metamorphic, sedimentary, and igneous rocks all over the world. Some of the historical sources include Australia, Brazil, England, Madagascar, Russia, Scotland, South Africa, Spain, Switzerland, and the United States, most notably in Arkansas.

All varieties of quartz are plentiful, so it is relatively easy to acquire excellent quality quartz at affordable prices. Look for vivid colors that appeal to you, and smooth surfaces and textures. For transparent varieties, look for stones that do not show visible inclusions (flaws). In the case of rose quartz, however, inclusions are usual and the stone should be evaluated on the color and smoothness of its surface. Whatever the specific type, a quartz stone set in a piece of jewelry should be visually pleasing and complement the earring, ring, pendant, or brooch mounting. The abundance of quartz and the subsequent availability of good- to high-quality stones allow the consumer to concentrate on attractiveness and style, without worrying about clarity gradings and technical color evaluations. Most varieties of quartz are a seven on the Mohs Scale and are considered a hard stone.

COLOR Quartz occurs naturally in many wonderful colors, including the following most popular varieties.
Black: Jet black, as well as the dark, to very dark gray varieties.
Ginger®: Golden brown.
Limon®: Yellow-green, reminiscent of the inside of a lime. This Brazilian variety is also referred to as *oro verde.*
Rose: Pale to medium pink.
Smoky: Gray-brown.

LEGEND AND LORE Quartz crystal is mentioned in the first-century text *Natural History,* written by the Roman philosopher Pliny. Quartz is known as the "Philosopher's Stone" and for a long time white quartz crystals were believed to show the future. Crystal balls used by seers were once made entirely of quartz — they are made of glass today. Psychics believe quartz can balance the body's chakras, or energy centers, and quartz stones of all kinds are believed to be stones of communication, both physical and spiritual. Quartz is often used to facilitate meditation and is believed to stimulate and amplify creativity. Quartz is also believed to be a healing stone that promotes clear observation and stability; specifically, smoky quartz can calm the mind, and rose quartz promotes serenity and love. Quartz is said to enhance self-confidence and personal authority.

SHAPE All varieties of quartz are cut into all the faceted gemstone shapes: round brilliant, oval, pear, marquise, emerald, heart, square, trillion, and fantasy. Some forms of quartz are also cut into cabochons and intaglios; carved into cameos, figurines, ash trays, and boxes; and fashioned into beads of various shapes.

WHAT IS RUBY? *Ruby is red corundum. The mineral corundum occurs in a wide range of colors, but all corundum that is not red is called sapphire (see Sapphire page 50). Ruby has long been prized as the "king of gems"— and because of its scarcity, large, vivid red rubies are more valuable than diamonds of the same size. Rubies above five carats are especially rare. Ruby is one of the three gemstones that comprise the trinity of colored stones; the other two are emerald and sapphire. (Diamonds are, of course, in a category all their own.) Rubies are beautiful, extremely hard, and exceptionally well-suited for use in jewelry of all kinds. Ruby is the July birthstone, the gemstone for the astrological sign of Leo, and the commemorative gemstone for the fifteenth and fortieth wedding anniversaries.*

ruby

Where is ruby found?
· · · · · · ·

Rubies are found in Myanmar—where ruby mines are older than recorded history—Sri Lanka, Thailand—the world's most important ruby trading center with eighty percent of the world's ruby trade passing through Thailand at some point — Afghanistan, India, Cambodia, Pakistan, Vietnam, Norway, Kenya, Tanzania, Australia and the United States.

LEGEND AND LORE Stories and legends abound about the precious ruby: Napoleon once gave Josephine a set of magnificent ruby jewelry; Sarah Ferguson ("Fergie") received a ruby engagement ring from Prince Andrew. A ruby weighing an astonishing 8,500 carats was carved in the shape of the Liberty Bell. The name of this magnificent stone? The Liberty Ruby, of course. Rubies have long been thought to bring health, financial success, wisdom, and success in love to their wearers. Rubies are also traditionally associated with passion, probably because of their intense red color. The ancients attributed magical powers to rubies, believing that the gemstone's red color would fade if its wearer was in danger or ill health, and that wearing a ruby on the left side, enabled a person to live in peace with his or her enemies. Rubies also symbolize beauty, charity, power, and royalty. To Christians, rubies are a sign of divine love. Rubies also have reputed medical powers, including the ability to protect wearers against plague, neutralize poisons, stop bleeding, and prevent pain.

COLOR Ruby occurs in several shades of red, including bright red, purplish red, brownish red, and pinkish red. Stones with vivid and consistent color throughout are considered the most attractive and are the most valuable.

SHAPE Ruby is extremely suitable for cutting into all the faceted gemstone shapes: round brilliant, oval, pear, marquise, emerald, heart, square, trillion, and fantasy. Ruby is also cut into cabochons, and some translucent rubies exhibit a six-line star effect in the middle when cut as a cabochon, which is actually the result of oriented internal inclusions. These gorgeous, intriguing stones are known as star rubies. The finest quality star rubies have stars with straight and equal-sized legs.

APPEAL The appeal of a ruby is its beautiful color and its exalted status as one of the rarest of stones. Pigeon's-blood red is a term used to describe a bright rich red free of purple or orange tints. In rubies, this pure bright red is less common and more desirable and those that are large and free of inclusions in addition, are the rarest and therefore the most valuable. Rubies are exceptionally durable stones; they measure nine on the Mohs Scale, meaning that only diamonds are harder. Rubies can be worn with confidence and can stand up to daily wear in rings, pendants, earrings, and other jewelry.

WHAT IS SAPPHIRE? *Sapphire is the name used for all colors of the mineral corundum — except red. (All red corundum is ruby.) When the term sapphire is used alone, it refers to a blue sapphire. All other colors of sapphire are called fancy sapphires collectively and use a color prefix in their individual names. Blue sapphire is the birthstone for September, the gemstone for the astrological sign of Taurus, and the commemorative gemstone for the fifth and forty-fifth wedding anniversaries.*

sapphire

Where is sapphire found?
. . . .

Sapphires of all colors are found in many places around the world, including Myanmar, Sri Lanka, India, Thailand, Australia, Madagascar, Nigeria, Cambodia, Brazil, Malawi, Colombia, China, Tanzania, and Montana in the United States. Australia is the source of nearly seventy percent of the world's sapphires.

Sapphire exists in a wide spectrum of beautiful colors. Blue sapphire is the most popular form of sapphire; fancy sapphires —as colors other than blue are called—are quite beautiful and also quite affordable. Fancy sapphires occur in shades of yellow, pink, green, violet, and white (colorless.) These fancies are identified by their color, as in green sapphire or white sapphire. White sapphire is the purest form of corundum. Some sapphires are identified by the region where they are mined, and regions are noted for the particular colors of sapphires mined there. Important sapphire localities include Kanchanaburi, Thailand; Australia; Myanmar, formerly called Burma; Sri Lanka, formerly Ceylon; Madagascar; the Kashmir region of India; Tanzania; and Montana in the United States.

Sapphire is cut into all the faceted gemstone shapes, with oval and marquise being the most common. Round brilliant, pear, emerald, heart, square, trillion, and fantasy cuts are also used for sapphires. Sapphire is also cut into cabochons and fashioned into beads of various shapes.

The appeal of sapphire in all its varieties is its wide array of glorious colors. The rarest blue sapphires are an intense blue, with no inclusions visible to the naked eye. The appeal of any given fancy sapphire lies in the intensity and uniformity of its color. A popular use for fancy sapphires is to mix them together in bracelets, rings, and brooches, resulting in a stunning rainbow effect. These striking multicolored pieces go with almost all complexions and colors of clothing.

LEGEND AND LORE Sapphires have long been considered guardians of good health. According to legend they have strong powers against poisons of all kinds and are said to be able to strengthen the eyes, stop nosebleeds, heal boils, treat ulcers and heart problems, alleviate swelling, and cure depression. Legend also holds that sapphires can provide comfort, courage, and strength, and protect sea travelers. Saint Jerome wrote that a sapphire could calm a person's enemies, and the gemstone has long been believed to be a powerful defense against sorcery, spells, witchcraft, and demons. Sapphires are also said to bestow spiritual enlightenment on their wearers, and to serve as a catalyst for wisdom. Buddhists believe that a sapphire can stimulate the desire to pray and can bring happiness and inner peace to the wearer. Sapphires are the gemstone of the Virgin Mary and are believed to assure peace, hope, truth, and prosperity. Sapphire is a lucky and supportive stone of archaeologists, historians, executives, ministers, and writers.

WHAT IS SPINEL? *Natural spinel is a mineral that occurs in a range of colors; it is often found when mining for corundum. Natural spinel should not be confused with synthetic spinel, which was created in 1910 as a diamond alternative and later made in colored varieties as a colored gemstone substitute. Spinel is quite hard — it registers seven and one-half to eight on the Mohs scale.*

spinel

Where is spinel found?

· · · · · · ·

The best sources for spinel are in Myanmar and Sri Lanka. Spinel is also found in Madagascar, Thailand, Cambodia, Afghanistan, Tanzania, Russia, Vietnam, Italy, Brazil, Sweden, Turkey, and the United States.

Spinel occurs in a range of attractive colors, including gray, orange, pink, purple, blue, green, black, and red. Bright red is a very popular but relatively rare spinel color. Cobalt blue spinel is currently the rarest color and also the most valuable variety of natural spinel. Orange spinel is known as flame spinel. There is also a type of spinel that changes color from gray-blue in daylight to purple under incandescent (artificial) light.

Spinel is cut into all the faceted gemstone shapes: round brilliant, oval, pear, marquise, emerald, heart, square, trillion, and fantasy. Spinel is also cut into cabochons and fashioned into beads of various shapes.

Many colors of spinel are quite plentiful, resulting in the availability of clean and lovely stones at affordable prices. The wide range of spinel's colors and the beauty of the stone make it an excellent alternative to higher-priced gemstones. Red spinel is a lovely alternative to ruby; cobalt blue spinel is too rare to be used in popular jewelry.

LEGEND AND LORE The gemstone spinel is associated mythologically with the planet Pluto and is believed to improve energy levels and boost physical strength during periods of extreme exertion, such as when exercising or performing strenuous physical work. Spinel also reputedly attracts money and wealth. Some of the differently colored spinel stones have their own lore. Blue or gray spinel is said to help the wearer cope with children, green spinel brings wisdom. Pink, red, and yellow spinel allegedly boost self-esteem. Purple spinel is believed to facilitate communicating with people older or younger than the wearer.

WHAT IS TANZANITE? *Tanzanite is the attractive, transparent, violet-blue variety of the mineral zoisite. It was first discovered in Tanzania at the foot of Mount Kilimanjaro in July 1967, and it reached the commercial market in the 1970s. It was named tanzanite by Tiffany's in honor of the stone's sole source, Tanzania. Tanzanite is not currently used as a birthstone, but it is the commemorative gemstone for the twenty-fourth wedding anniversary*

tanzanite

Where is tanzanite found?
· · · · · · ·
Violet-blue tanzanite is found in Tanzania and Madagascar.

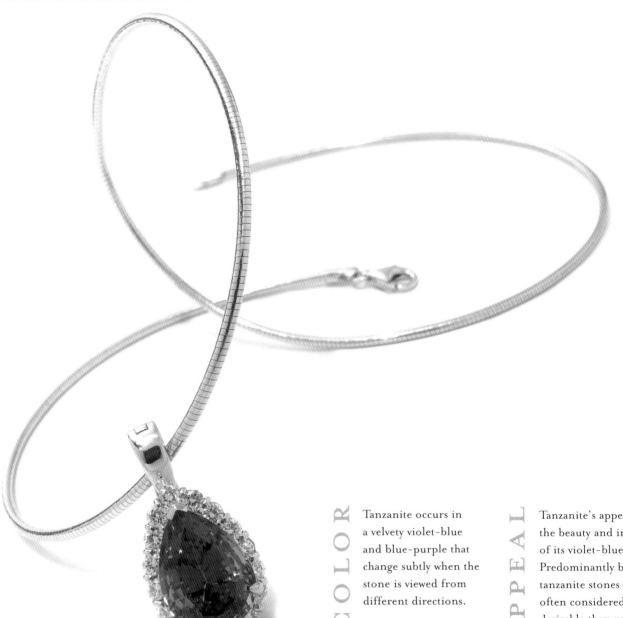

LEGEND AND LORE Even though it is a relatively new gemstone, lore has already sprung up around tanzanite. According to information channeled by a psychic known simply as "Michael" and compiled by Dr. Judithann David, tanzanite can balance the emotions and tone down the excessive drive that makes some people operate at too frantic a pace.

SHAPE

COLOR

Tanzanite occurs in a velvety violet-blue and blue-purple that change subtly when the stone is viewed from different directions.

Tanzanite is cut into all the faceted gemstone shapes: round brilliant, oval, pear, marquise, emerald, heart, square, trillion, and fantasy. The hardness rating for tanzanite on the Mohs scale is between six and six and one-half, making it suitable for earrings, pendants, brooches, and in protected mountings, for rings.

APPEAL

Tanzanite's appeal lies in the beauty and intensity of its violet-blue color. Predominantly blue tanzanite stones are often considered more desirable than predominantly violet stones. The violet-blue hue of tanzanite is very attractive to those looking for a stone between deep blue sapphires and intensely purple amethysts.

WHAT IS TIGER'S-EYE? *Tiger's-eye is a pseudomorph, which means false form, of a fibrous mineral called crocidolite. The crocidolite has been replaced by quartz, but the original fibrous structure remains. This structure can create a cat's-eye when the stone is cut into a cabochon.*

tiger's-eye

Where is tiger's-eye found?
· · · · · · ·
Tiger's-eye is found in South Africa, Sri Lanka, India, Brazil, Australia, and the United States.

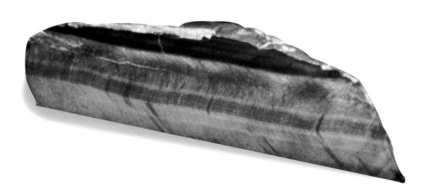

LEGEND AND LORE Tiger's-eye is associated with the sun and is believed to soften stubbornness. Tiger's-eye allegedly also promotes physical healing and facilitates the relaxation response, allowing people who are under stress to unwind. Tiger's-eye is believed to provide protection against danger of all kinds and to promote courage and self-confidence in the wearer. Roman soldiers wore engraved tiger's-eye stones to protect them during battle. The gemstone is used to bring luck to the wearer and is believed to attract money and wealth. Tiger's-eye is also said to promote strong energy flow throughout the body, stimulate clear vision, and encourage insight; some have used it to assist in the remembering of past lives. Tiger's-eye is a lucky and supportive stone for detectives, divers, and those who work on or near the water.

COLOR Tiger's-eye occurs naturally in a range of browns, including golden brown, yellowish-brown, and reddish-brown. It also occurs in a bluish form known as hawk's-eye. A honey brown with dark banding is a very popular form of tiger's-eye, and is often used in men's jewelry, such as cufflinks and tie tacks.

APPEAL The appeal of cabochon-cut tiger's-eye is the distinctiveness and beauty of its "eye", and its unique texture. Tiger's-eye stones are often set in earrings and rings, and larger stones make lovely and unique brooches. Smaller matching oval stones are sometimes set together in tennis bracelets for a unique and dramatic look.

SHAPE Tiger's-eye is cut into cabochons (to highlight the "eye" effect) cut and polished into beads, and carved into figurines and flat tablets with a wavy "eye" effect.

WHAT IS TOPAZ? *Topaz is a mineral that occurs in a wide range of glorious colors. Topaz is moderately priced and readily available in most colors and shapes, although the pink variety is rarer. The yellow variety of topaz, known as champagne or golden topaz, is used as the November birthstone; in recent years, blue topaz has replaced turquoise as the December birthstone.*

topaz

Where is topaz found?
· · · · · · ·

Topaz is found in the United States, Brazil, Sri Lanka, Myanmar, The Urals, Transbaikalia, Australia, Pakistan, Mexico, Japan, and Africa. Today, much of the finest quality topaz comes from Brazil.

Topaz is available in many gorgeous shades of yellow, orange, brown, pink, and blue. Topaz also occurs in a colorless state. There are several variations of topaz used for jewelry, including imperial (a combination of orange and pink), and golden topaz (an orange-gold), Swiss blue topaz (a medium blue), sky blue topaz (a pale blue that resembles aquamarine), and London blue topaz (a rich, deep blue).

Topaz is valued for its wide range of colors and its beautiful transparency. It is possible to find clean, brilliant blue topaz stones at affordable prices. The availability of so many colors makes topaz a suitable stone for any style of fashion and all complexions. Topaz is set into earrings, rings, brooches, pendants, and bracelets. It is a versatile gemstone that makes a wonderful addition to any jewelry wardrobe.

LEGEND AND LORE Topaz's name is believed to be derived from Topazius, the ancient Greek name for the island of Zabargad in the Red Sea, because of a mistaken belief that the gemstone mined there was topaz. (It was really peridot.) Topaz is known as the "fire stone" because to the ancient Hindus, topaz signified fire. Not surprisingly then, it is believed that a topaz in your home will protect it from fire. Topaz is also said to have wondrous healing powers. It is believed to relieve the pain of rheumatism and arthritis, and regulate the digestive system. Topaz is also said to prevent colds, restore physical strength, and even aid in weight loss. Legend holds that if you place a topaz under your pillow at night, you will not sleepwalk or have nightmares. This trick can also be used to alleviate stress. Topaz is believed to protect against injury, sudden death, and evil spells. Topaz is believed to draw love to the wearer, aid communication in personal relationships, and eliminate fear, anger, and greed. Topaz is also believed to improve a wearer's relationship with animals. Topaz is a lucky and supportive stone for actors, government workers, radio and TV workers, and salespeople.

Topaz is cut into all the faceted gemstone shapes, including round brilliant, oval, emerald, cushion, marquise, pear, and trillion.

WHAT IS TOURMALINE? *Tourmaline is a mineral that is popular as a gemstone. It occurs in a complete range of colors, a colorless form, as well as multicolored varieties. Pink tourmaline is one of the stones used as the October birthstone; tourmaline is the commemorative gemstone for the eighth wedding anniversary.*

tourmaline

Where is tourmaline found?
• • • • • • •

Tourmaline is found in many places around the world, including Brazil, the United States, Sri Lanka, Canada, Mexico, Australia, Myanmar, Madagascar, Nigeria, Tanzania, and Namibia.

LEGEND AND LORE The name tourmaline comes from the Singhalese word *turmali,* which means "mixed precious stones." The legends surrounding tourmaline, and the powers attributed to these beautiful gemstones, are many and varied. Blue tourmaline is believed to assist wearers in distancing themselves from negative people and events, and to bring peace of mind. Green tourmaline can reputedly aid communication, attract money and wealth, and ensure success in business. (Some people place a green tourmaline in their coin jars or wallets.) Green tourmaline is also believed to stimulate creativity. Pink tourmaline is said to relax the wearer and relieve tension, and also attract love and friendship. Red tourmaline is said to spur courage and strengthen self-confidence. Watermelon tourmaline reputedly has the power to balance the male and female energies present in every individual, and to attract love. Watermelon tourmaline is also believed to promote stamina and bestow the wearer with an aura of dependability and maturity. Tourmaline is a lucky and supportive stone for miners and telephone workers.

COLOR Tourmaline occurs in a gorgeous rainbow of colors, including all the shades of green (chrome tourmaline is an especially vivid green due to the presence of chromium); red (rubellite); shades of pink; blue (indicolite); shades of yellow, orange, brown (dravite); golden yellow; colorless (achroite); and multicolored. An important multicolored variety is bicolored tourmaline. Watermelon tourmaline, which has bands of green and pink that make it look exactly like the inside of watermelon, is the most prized of the bicolored tourmalines.

SHAPE Tourmaline is cut into all the faceted gemstone shapes: round brilliant, oval, pear, marquise, emerald, heart, square, trillion, and fantasy. Watermelon tourmaline is also cut into flat tablets. Cat's-eye tourmaline is cut into cabochons.

APPEAL Tourmaline is popular because of its wonderful colors. Tourmaline occurs with a wide range of inclusions, as well as colors; almost all pink and red tourmalines have internal inclusions of varying degrees of visi-bility. These should be viewed as natural markings that add to the charm and uniqueness of an individual stone.

WHAT IS TURQUOISE? *Turquoise is an opaque, blue to bluish green mineral. It is one of the few gemstones that is completely opaque. Turquoise has long been associated with Native American jewelry and is currently extremely popular for setting in sterling silver. Turquoise is the traditional December birthstone and is the commemorative gemstone for the eleventh wedding anniversary.*

turquoise

Where is turquoise found?
• • • • • • •

Through the ages, the finest turquoise has come from the Middle East, where it has been mined since at least 1000 B.C. Turquoise of varying colors is also found in Mexico, China, Russia, Chile, Australia, and in the southwest United States, especially New Mexico and Arizona. Currently, the southwest United States is the world's largest source of turquoise.

COLOR Turquoise occurs in shades of blue, with medium blue being the most well known and popular color. Turquoise also is found in shades from blue-green to green.

SHAPE The cabochon cut is the most popular shape used for turquoise. It is also cut and polished into beads of various shapes. Turquoise is often set into bezels, which help protect the stone.

APPEAL The appeal of turquoise stones lies in their blue color and smooth cabochon shapes. Turquoise looks lovely in sterling silver and is equally striking when set in yellow gold. Popular uses for turquoise include rings, earrings, pendants brooches, and bracelets. Turquoise is enjoying a resurgence in high-end pieces where it is set in gold and platinum.

LEGEND AND LORE Turquoise, which has been cherished by almost every culture throughout history, was found in the Sinai Peninsula in what is now Egypt over six thousand years ago, and it has been mined in Iran for over three thousand years. Turquoise was called *fayruz* in ancient Arabic, or "lucky stone." Pueblo Indians placed a turquoise stone under the floor when they built a new house to petition the Great Spirit for protection for all who lived there. Native Americans revere turquoise because they believe their souls become one with the universe when they wear the beautiful blue stone, and Apache shamans have always carried turquoise in their medicine bags. An Oriental proverb says that a turquoise given by a loving hand brings happiness and good fortune. Turquoise is a powerful protective stone for travelers embarking on journeys to dangerous places, and it is believed to guard against the evil eye, disease, and accidents. Turquoise can allegedly cure migraines and reduce fevers, and some believe that drinking water in which a piece of turquoise has been dipped has curative powers. Turquoise is a lucky and supportive stone for accountants, computer operators, physical laborers, and radio and TV workers.

WHAT IS ZIRCON? *Zircon is a transparent mineral that occurs naturally in many colors, as well as in a colorless form. Zircon is not the same stone as cubic zirconia, which is a man-made gemstone. Colorless zircon was once a very popular diamond substitute because of the visual similarities between the two stones. Blue zircon is used as a December birthstone and it has been used as the commemorative gemstone for the seventh wedding anniversary.*

zircon

Where is zircon found?
. . . .

Zircon is found in Sri Lanka, Myanmar, Thailand, Cambodia, Vietnam, Australia, Brazil, Nigeria, Tanzania, and France. Bangkok, Thailand, is the world's center for cutting and exporting zircon stones.

LEGEND AND LORE Wearers of zircon are believed to be blessed with uncommon wisdom and honor. Zircon is also said to lessen labor pains and protect from evil spirits. As with other multicolored stones, every color of zircon is believed to possess different powers. White zircon is worn for protection and is used to promote logical and sharp thinking. Brown and yellow zircon are said to banish headaches, stimulate the libido, attract romance and love, and alleviate depression. Green zircon can allegedly eliminate shyness and also attract money to the wearer. Blue zircon is believed to help priests and the religious in their pastoral duties, while pink zircon is used to aid spiritual growth. Red zircon is said to cure ear infections, as well as to increase wealth and protect the wearer from injuries. Orange zircon is reputed to have the power to enhance the beauty of the wearer and to protect his or her home from thieves. Zircon is a lucky and protective stone of detectives and homemakers.

COLOR Zircon occurs naturally in a wide range of subtle colors, including blue, yellow, orange, brown, green, and tones of red or brownish-red. It also occurs in a colorless variety, known as white zircon.

SHAPE Zircon is cut into all the faceted gemstone shapes: round brilliant, oval, pear, marquise, emerald, heart, square, trillion, and fantasy.

APPEAL Zircons have unusually high dispersion or fire. As with other transparent stones, zircon is appreciated for its glorious rainbow of colors. The use of zircons in jewelry is somewhat limited, although prices of zircon jewelry are reasonable.

unique favorite

g e

These gems have life in them: their colours speak,

say what words fail of.

GEORGE ELIOT,
The Spanish Gypsy

stones

WHAT IS AMAZONITE? *Amazonite, which is named for the Amazon River, is a mineral that is found in Brazil, but oddly enough, not near the Amazon River. Amazonite occurs in translucent to opaque specimens, and because of its color, it is sometimes confused with turquoise and jade.*

amazonite

Where is amazonite found?
. . . .

Besides Brazil, amazonite is found in the United States, Canada, Madagascar, India, Russia, and Africa, especially Tanzania, Namibia, and in the Sahara Desert in northern Africa.

COLOR Amazonite has a unique texture and occurs in lovely pastel shades of blue-green, as well as in a pale green that resembles the color of jade.

SHAPE Amazonite is cut into cabochons and also fashioned and polished into beads of various shapes. It is rarely used for carving or for faceted shapes.

APPEAL The appeal of amazonite is its lovely color, smooth texture, and characteristic gridlike surface patterns. It is excellent for wear in earrings, pendants, and brooches. However, because this gemstone is not very hard—only measures around a six on the Mohs scale—rings set with amazonite can be delicate and should be worn with care.

LEGEND AND LORE Amazonite is mythologically associated with the planet Uranus and is believed to make the wearer more aware of self-destructive habits and to bestow the strength to eliminate such traits. Amazonite is also a good luck talisman, worn by gamblers and by people embarking on a new venture or starting a new career. Amazonite is also known as the "hope stone" and is believed to assist the wearer in dealing with daily challenges.

WHAT IS AMETRINE? *Ametrine is a combination of purple quartz (amethyst) and yellow quartz (citrine) in one gemstone. It has only been commercially available for the past twenty years. The unique natural pairing of the purple and yellow colors gives ametrine its especially interesting and appealing look.*

ametrine

Where is ametrine found?
· · · · · · ·
Even though amethyst and citrine are found all over the world, the main source of ametrine is Bolivia, although it was first discovered in Brazil in 1979.

LEGEND AND LORE Perhaps because it is
a natural blend of two different stones, ametrine
is believed to help families welcome new members
from different ethnic or cultural backgrounds.
In addition, because ametrine is actually amethyst
and citrine in one gemstone, it is believed to
manifest the spiritual aspects of amethyst along
with the healing properties of citrine.

COLOR Ametrine occurs
naturally as a purple
and yellow gemstone.
It is cut to emphasize
this natural color
phenomenon.

APPEAL The unique and
lovely coloration of
ametrine is its special
appeal. Stones with
vivid and distinct color
contrast are considered
the most unusual and
desirable ametrines.

SHAPE Ametrine's natural quartz
structure allows it to be
cut into all the faceted
shapes, as well as fashioned
into beads and used for
cabochons. Emerald,
or rectangular cuts are
preferred for stones that
have distinctive color
separation. The emerald
cut displays the two
natural colors of ametrine
side-by-side, maximizing
the color contrast and
giving the stone its most
striking look.

WHAT IS ANDALUSITE? *Andalusite is a unique, yellow-brown to olive green, transparent mineral that can exhibit different colors when viewed from various angles. Because of this fascinating ability to apparently change colors, andalusite is sometimes called the poor man's alexandrite.*

andalusite

Where is andalusite found?
· · · · · · ·
Andalusite is found in Sri Lanka, Brazil, Russia, Spain, Canada, Australia, and the United States.

LEGEND AND LORE Andalusite is believed to be a powerful tool for those striving to build a career or start a business. It reputedly enhances the wearer's ability to be discriminating in all things and to marshal power in the most effective ways. Andalusite is believed to strengthen the will and increase personal perseverance, as well as to help the wearer maintain focus and stay centered on goals.

COLOR

Andalusite occurs in a range of colors, including yellow-brown, olive green, and reddish-brown. In some cases, red, yellow, and green can appear in a single stone under the same light source, depending on the angle from which it is viewed.

SHAPE

Andalusite is cut into many of the faceted gem-stone shapes, including round brilliant, emerald, square, and octagon.

APPEAL

The appeal of andalusite lies in its beautiful, subtle colors and its unique ability to display different colors in one stone. Some stones exhibit different hues when turned and viewed from various angles. Andalusite is also a fairly durable stone (a seven on the Mohs Scale for hardness) making it suitable for rings, as well as earrings, pendants, and brooches.

WHAT IS APATITE? *Apatite is a mineral that occurs in a range from totally opaque, through translucent, to completely transparent stones. It exists in a wide range of colors and is one of the few gemstones that can be cut both in a faceted style as well en cabochon which can demonstrate a cat's-eye effect.*

apatite

Where is apatite found?
· · · · · · ·

Apatite is mined in Myanmar, Sri Lanka, Brazil, Russia, Canada, Africa, Germany, Sweden, Spain, Switzerland, Mexico, Madagascar and the United States.

Apatite is believed to bless its wearer with the ability to accept whatever comes, with patience and grace. Apatite is believed to bring inner peace through a calm and poised stoicism.

COLOR Apatite occurs in several colors, including yellow, brown, blue, pink, violet, purple, green, and color-less. Apatite can be cut into cabochons to show a cat's-eye pattern. The yellow-green variety of apatite, found primarily in Spain, is known as asparagus stone.

SHAPE Apatite is cut into all the faceted gemstone shapes: round brilliant, oval, pear, marquise, emerald, heart, square, trillion, and fantasy. Blue, green, and yellow apatite is also cut into cabochons when the stones have inclusions that will create a cat's-eye effect.

APPEAL The appeal of faceted apatite stones is in the vividness of the individual stone's color. The appeal of neon blue apatites is the smoothness of the stone's surface and the distinctiveness of color. Apatite is a delicate stone —only a five on the Mohs scale—so pendants, earrings, and brooches are the best way to wear apatite of whatever color. When apatite is made into rings, protective settings are used.

WHAT IS CARNELIAN? *Carnelian is a chalcedony that is brownish-orange or red. It is an affordable and attractive stone that is popular for use in pendants and brooches. Carnelian can be similar in appearance to some coral, but it is a mined stone and may exhibit color banding. Carnelian is one of the most popular of the chalcedonies.*

carnelian

Where is carnelian found?
• • • • • • •
Carnelian is mined in India; it is also found in Brazil and Uruguay.

Carnelian occurs in shades of brownish-orange or brownish-red. In some cases color banding permeates the stone.

The beauty of carnelian is in its rich, even color. The more appealing carnelians have deep and uniform color through-out the stone.

Carnelian is cut into cabochons, fashioned and polished into beads, and carved into cameos, scarabs, and intaglios. Carnelian may also be used for inlay work or cut into faceted shapes, although, because it is often very close to opaque, light does not pass through most carnelian stones. Carnelians are cut into faceted shapes for the appeal of the form, not to display translucency.

LEGEND AND LORE Carnelian's name comes from the Latin word for flesh. Carnelians were worn by architects in ancient Egypt to signify their elevated rank. The Moslem prophet Muhammad wore a carnelian ring set in silver. Carnelians are believed to be able to bestow courage and a strong and confident speaking voice, as well as to enhance self-worth and self-confidence. Carnelian is also believed to balance the emotions, calm the temper, and even stop bleeding. Carnelian is a lucky and supportive stone for architects, athletes, builders, construction workers, government workers, journalists, military personnel, and salespeople.

WHAT IS CHRYSOPRASE? *Chrysoprase is a translucent to opaque form of green chalcedony that sometimes resembles jade. It has become very popular with American jewelry designers in recent years.*

chrysoprase

Where is chrysoprase found?
· · · · · · ·

Chrysoprase has been found in Germany, Russia, Brazil, Canada, Austria, and in California in the United States. Stones that boast a gorgeous apple green color are mined in Queensland in western Australia.

LEGEND AND LORE Chrysoprase's name comes from the Greek words *chrysos,* "golden" and *prason,* "leek", a reference to the stone's striking color. Many ancient cultures believed that possessing and wearing chrysoprase would bring good fortune and prosperity. Legend has it that Alexander the Great wore a chrysoprase stone in his belt to ensure victory in battle. In the 1800s, great protective powers were attributed to chrysoprase: rumor held that a condemned criminal could escape beheading or hanging by placing a chrysoprase in his or her mouth immediately prior to being led to execution. It is also believed that chrysoprase can strengthen the heart and heal emotional wounds of all kinds. Medicinal powers are also attributed to chrysoprase, including the power to improve vision, stop bleeding, and alleviate the pain of rheumatism. According to legend, wearers of chrysoprase become incredibly articulate, supremely compassionate, and brimming with love and wisdom.

COLOR Chrysoprase occurs in lovely shades of green and yellow-green, from pale hues to vivid apple green.

SHAPE Chrysoprase is usually cut into cabochons, or fashioned into beads of all shapes. Chrysoprase may also be used for cameos and intaglios, and in inlay work.

APPEAL The appeal of chrysoprase, besides its affordability, lies in its beautiful range of green and its popular cabochon shape. Chrysoprase is made into lovely and dramatic rings, pendants, and brooches. Thin slices of green chrysoprase are also used for mosaic designs and inlay work.

WHAT IS IOLITE? *Iolite is an attractive, transparent, violet-blue mineral. Iolite is sometimes called water sapphire because it resembles blue sapphire when viewed face up. Iolite is the commemorative gemstone for the twenty-first wedding anniversary.*

iolite

Where is iolite found?

Iolite is found in Sri Lanka, Myanmar, India, Madagascar, Brazil, Namibia, Tanzania, Zimbabwe, Germany, Norway, Finland, and the United States.

APPEAL Iolite's appeal lies in its lovely color and its affordability. The best specimens are spectacular. Iolite is a rising star of contemporary gemstone jewelry, proven by its growing popularity in rings, earrings, bracelets, and pendants.

COLOR Iolite occurs in a range of colors from medium violet-blue to deep blue. Some stones have a gray tint.

SHAPE Iolite is cut into most of the faceted gemstone shapes, including round brilliant, oval, pear, marquise, and emerald. Iolite is also cut into cabochons.

LEGEND AND LORE Iolite's name comes from the Greek word *ios* which means "violet." Iolite was once called "Viking's compass." Viking explorers would look through thin slices of iolite to find the position of the sun on cloudy days; the stone would filter out the haze and allow the sun to be seen. Iolite is believed to be a leadership stone, which can make the wearer supremely confident, strong-willed, and capable. The deep blue forms of iolite are believed to strengthen friendships.

WHAT IS KUNZITE? *Kunzite is a lovely, transparent, lilac pink gemstone form of the mineral spodumene. Kunzite was first discovered in 1877 in Brazil and is named after George Frederick Kunz, the California gemologist and former vice-president of Tiffany's, who first identified the stone in 1902.*

kunzite

Where is kunzite found?
. . . .

Kunzite is found in Brazil, Myanmar, Madagascar, Afghanistan, Canada, Mexico, Sweden, and the United States.

APPEAL

The appeal of kunzite is in its delicate colors and modest cost. Faceted pink kunzite stones are lovely and dramatic and make wonderful pendants. The affordable prices of kunzite give jewelry lovers (especially those who love the colors lilac and pink) the opportunity to own large, impressive stones for reasonable prices.

COLOR

Kunzite occurs in a range of pinks from pale to light and lilac pink, to lilac.

SHAPE

Kunzite is cut into many of the faceted gemstone shapes, including round brilliant, oval, pear, marquise, step, and emerald.

LEGEND AND LORE Kunzite is associated with the planets Venus and Pluto, and is believed to be a grounding stone with the power to calm and center the emotions. Kunzite is reputed to act as a gemological tranquilizer, capable of relaxing the wearer. Simply carrying a kunzite or staring at a kunzite stone is said to calm fears, ease tensions, and banish worries. Some holistic healers rub kunzite over tight muscles to relax them. Kunzite is also thought to attract love and enhance romance.

WHAT IS MARCASITE? *In the jewelry trade, what is sold under the name of marcasite is actually iron pyrite. The mineral marcasite is less stable than iron pyrite and is almost never used in contemporary jewelry. Today, marcasite (iron pyrite) is used when a shiny metallic look is desired.*

marcasite

Where is marcasite found?
· · · · · · ·

Marcasite, or iron pyrite, is found in clay and limestone all over the world.

Marcasite—the name used for iron pyrite in jewelry —is shiny and usually appears gray to grayish black in color.

Marcasite stones, with their metallic luster, make lovely accents when set with colored stones. Some of the colored stones commonly combined in settings with marcasite include amethyst, black onyx, blue topaz, citrine, garnet, iolite, lapis, malachite, mother-of-pearl, opal, pearl, peridot, sapphire, smoky quartz, and a variety of simulated gemstones. Marcasite can also be quite dramatic on its own when several stones are set together in sterling silver, as in a brooch or a bracelet.

Stones are cut into square or round faceted shapes and then usually set into sterling silver to maximize their reflective quality.

LEGEND AND LORE Marcasite was used in jewelry by the Incas and the ancient Greeks. The ancient Mexicans used iron pyrite to make mirrors, and the ancient Chinese believed that it could protect against crocodile attacks. Marcasite was extremely popular during the Victorian period of nineteenth century England, and many of the most sought-after antique jewelry pieces from that era feature marcasite. The powers attributed to marcasite include the ability to attract money and good luck.

WHAT IS MOONSTONE? *Moonstone is a shimmering, opalescent form of feldspar that occurs in a range of colors but is extremely popular in its white to blue forms. Moonstone displays a phenomenon called adularescence that makes light appear to float within the stone as it is viewed from different angles.*

moonstone

Where is moonstone found?

· · · · · · ·

The two major sources of moonstone are Sri Lanka and Myanmar. It is also found in India, Madagascar, Brazil, Mexico, Norway, Tanzania, Kenya, Russia, throughout the Swiss and French Alps, and in the United States.

LEGEND AND LORE Moonstone, known as the "Traveler's stone", was believed to be metaphysically connected to the moon – thus the name. Legend has it that the phases of the moon can actually be seen in the stone as the month passes: at the new moon, a small white spot appears in the stone and grows larger in the moonstone as the moon grows larger in the night sky. Moonstone's power to attract love was said to increase as the moon grew larger. The ancient Romans believed that moonstone held the image of their moon goddess Diana within it; the stone has also been associated with the other moon goddesses, the Greek goddess Selene and the Egyptian Isis. Moonstones are believed to bring romance into their wearers' lives and to help reconcile lovers who have parted in anger. A moonstone placed under the pillow is said to assure sound sleep. Moonstones are alleged to clear the mind and assist in logical thinking.

COLOR

Moonstone occurs in several colors, including blue, white, green, gray, peach, and yellow.

SHAPE

The most popular cut for moonstone is the cabochon, polished into an oval domed shape, which shows off its wondrous adularescence. Moonstone may also be cut and fashioned into beads, used for cameos, or cut into round faceted shapes that display its adularescence on the stone's crown or top.

APPEAL

Moonstone's appeal lies in its unique billowy light and lovely pastel colors. Moonstones are often bezel set in rings because the movement of the hand accents the play-of-light and color in the stone. Other popular uses for moonstones include pendants and brooches.

WHAT IS MORGANITE? *Morganite is a lovely, transparent, pink form of beryl, named after the financier J. Pierpont Morgan, a gem aficionado and collector.*

morganite

Where is morganite found?
· · · · · · ·

The finest morganite is found in Madagascar; it is also mined in Afghanistan, Brazil, Italy, Madagascar, Mozambique, Namibia, Zimbabwe, Pakistan, Russia, and the United States.

Morganite occurs in a range of pinks, from a pale to a deeper pink, and a light to a deeper peach.

Morganite's appeal is its striking pink pastel colors, which complement all complexions and provide a subtle touch of color to many fashion styles.

Morganite is cut into many of the faceted gemstone shapes, including round brilliant, oval, pear, marquise, step, and emerald.

LEGEND AND LORE The legends surrounding beryl go back as far as the thirteenth century. All types of beryl were long believed to aid negotiations and provide a strong psychic defense against enemies. Beryl was said to improve the wearer's thinking and inspire productivity. Morganite, a pink beryl and a relatively modern stone, shares these mythical powers. Gem lovers believe it to be capable of making the wearer more tolerant and less prejudiced.

WHAT IS RHODONITE? *Rhodonite is a pink- to rose-red form of manganese silicate that can range from translucent to opaque. Rhodonite is becoming quite popular and is used more and more for contemporary pendants, brooches, rings, and for strands of beads.*

rhodonite

Where is rhodonite found?
· · · · · · ·

Rhodonite is mined in the Ural Mountains in Russia, as well as in Sweden, Australia, the United States, India, South Africa, Japan, New Zealand, and England.

LEGEND AND LORE Rhodonite's name comes from the Greek word *rhodos,* which means "rose." Rhodonite is associated with the planet Mars and is said to help the wearer project a cultivated and refined demeanor. Rhodonite is believed to reduce stress and allow the wearer to stay calm in especially trying circumstances. Rhodonite is also associated with the power to clarify confusing situations and emotions and alleviate self-doubt. It is said to enhance the wearer's communication skills by promoting inner balance and coherence. Rhodonite is a lucky and supportive stone for waiters and waitresses.

COLOR Rhodonite occurs in shades of pink, from light to dark. Many specimens also have black lines and lacy patterns traced throughout the stone. Some rhodonite stones have areas of varying color, resulting in an attractive dappled effect.

APPEAL The appeal of rhodonite is in its color, or colors. Rhodonite stones with dappled pinks are particularly appealing and rhodonite's characteristic black tracings can also be quite striking.

SHAPE Rhodonite is cut into cabochons and fashioned and polished into beads. It is also used for carving cameos and intaglios.

WHAT ARE SCARABS? *A scarab is the name given to any of a variety of gemstones cut into a cabochon shape and carved with a beetle design on the top. Some also have a seal or date carved on the back. In nature, a scarab is a type of beetle and scarab carving has an age-old history, harkening back to the ancient Egyptians who revered the insect as a symbol of the sun god.*

scarab

The different gemstones cut into scarab cabochons include:

• • • • • • •

Agate, sodalite, lapis lazuli (blues)
Black onyx, (black)
Calcite (white)
Carnelian, red jasper (reds)
Chrysoprase, green aventurine (greens)
Jasper, rhodonite, rhodochrosite (pinks)
Quartz, quartzite (varied colors)
Tiger's-eye, yellow jasper (yellows)

Scarabs are set into bracelets, pendants, earrings, and watch bracelets.

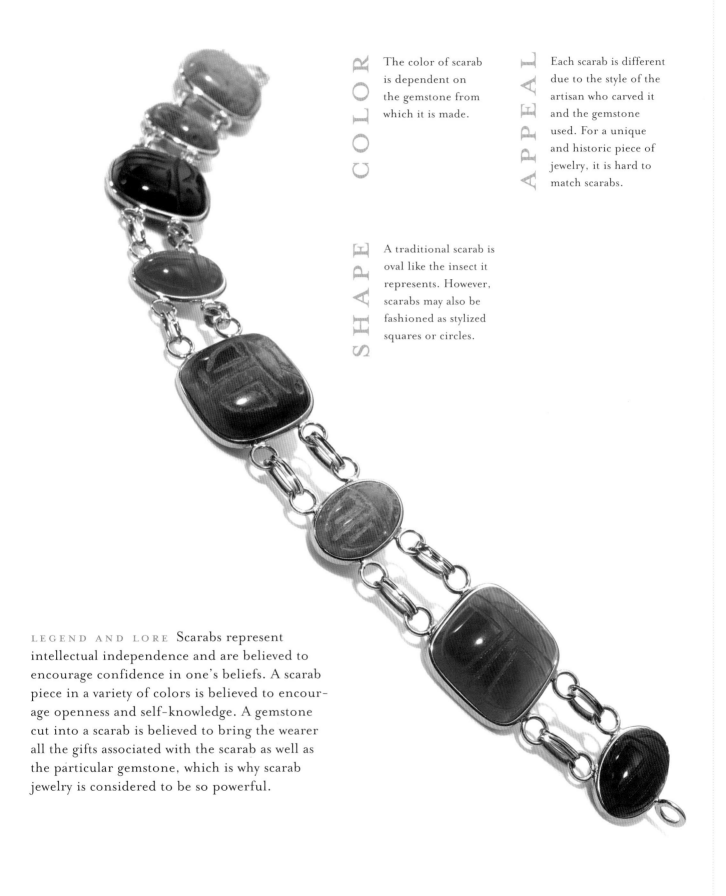

The color of scarab is dependent on the gemstone from which it is made.

Each scarab is different due to the style of the artisan who carved it and the gemstone used. For a unique and historic piece of jewelry, it is hard to match scarabs.

A traditional scarab is oval like the insect it represents. However, scarabs may also be fashioned as stylized squares or circles.

LEGEND AND LORE Scarabs represent intellectual independence and are believed to encourage confidence in one's beliefs. A scarab piece in a variety of colors is believed to encourage openness and self-knowledge. A gemstone cut into a scarab is believed to bring the wearer all the gifts associated with the scarab as well as the particular gemstone, which is why scarab jewelry is considered to be so powerful.

WHAT IS SUGILITE? *Sugilite (pronounced sue-ji-lite) is a translucent to opaque, deep purple to purple-red gemstone that is colored by manganese. It was named for the Japanese petrologist Ken-ichi Sugi, who first discovered the stone in the 1970s.*

sugilite

Where is sugilite found?
· · · · · · ·
Almost all gem sugilite comes from South Africa.

Sugilite occurs in a range of purples, from a deep, vivid purple to a reddish-purple.

Due to its opaque nature, sugilite is usually cut into cabochons and fashioned into beads.

The appeal of sugilite is its rich, warm purple colors; sugilite stones have the appeal of the most dramatic amethysts, but in an opaque form. Sugilite makes lovely rings and pendants when set into sterling silver, and strands of sugilite beads are also very distinctive.

LEGEND AND LORE Sugilite is believed to bring out its wearer's psychic abilities as well as to enhance meditation and foster wisdom and spirituality.

This is that happy morn,

That day, long-wished day...

Which, purely white, deserves

An everlasting diamond should it mark.

WILLIAM DRUMMOND,
Summons to Love

diamond

revealed

Diamond, known as the king of gems, is the hardest
mineral on earth. On the Mohs Scale of gemstone
hardness, diamonds are the ultimate standard: Diamonds
are a ten on the Mohs Scale—the maximum rating—
all other natural gemstones are ranked lower.

A diamond is made of simple carbon. It takes 250 tons
of ore to find a single crystal to make a one-carat polished
diamond. Only one in one thousand diamonds weighs
over one carat. Diamonds are mined all over the world
including India, Russia, Australia, Canada, Brazil, and
many countries in Africa.

Rough diamonds barely hint at the hidden glories waiting to be revealed in the dull white stone, but the crystalline structure of a diamond lends itself magnificently to cutting and polishing. After a diamond has been finished by a master cutter, the results can range from an included, small stone to a flawless, large stone. Regardless of the quality of the finished stone, however, there is no denying that a cut and polished diamond is one of the most beautiful objects on earth.

Diamonds were first mined in India almost three thousand years ago. Early attempts at cutting and polishing diamonds resulted in blocklike cuts such as table cuts, rose cuts, old mine cuts, and old European cuts. These older cuts did not have the visual appeal of today's modern cuts. Technology has allowed diamond cutters to perfect the cutting and polishing process. Now it is possible to produce the best possible finished stone from an uncut diamond crystal.

Diamonds have long been treasured as symbols of eternal love, and the diamond engagement ring is a beloved part of courting and marriage rituals. De Beers uses "A diamond is forever" as their slogan emphasizing the fact that diamonds were formed hundreds of million of years ago — and so, are the perfect way to say "I will always love you."

Diamonds are used for much more than engagement rings, though. Diamond earrings and diamond pendants are perennially popular and are important parts of every woman's jewelry wardrobe. Diamonds are also used as accent stones in colored gemstone rings, pendants, and earrings. The diamond wedding band is another popular contemporary use of diamonds.

Throughout history, diamonds have been cherished, and not only for their beauty. The myths, legends, and lore surrounding diamonds could fill volumes. It is really not at all surprising that such an incredible natural creation as a diamond should be so revered that people have attributed mystical and magical qualities to it.

According to legend, wearing a diamond endows the wearer with unparalleled strength, bravery, and courage. Diamonds are also reputed to possess spiritual qualities that can repel demons and evil spirits. Diamonds can supposedly attract friends, guarantee success, imbue the wearer with an aura of authority and power, and assure good fortune. Diamonds are rumored to slow down the aging process and also to bring wealth to the wearer. They are believed to assure invincibility, encourage spirituality, and—perhaps most intriguingly, considering that diamonds symbolize everlasting love—enhance sexual prowess in both the giver and the recipient.

The diamond is perhaps the most important natural gemstone used in jewelry. The following sections will explain the many sizes, shapes, qualities, and colors of diamonds. Diamonds are evaluated by what has come to be known as the "Four Cs": *color, clarity, cut,* and *carat weight.* But before getting started there are a few terms you should know.

BLEMISH
An external *clarity characteristic on a diamond.*

CLEAVAGE
The natural tendency of a crystal to break along a certain plane. Diamonds have perfect cleavage, and a skillful diamond cutter can separate a stone into two parts—and each will have a flat surface. Although it is the hardest gemstone, and virtually impervious to scratches, even a diamond is not indestructible. After a diamond has been cut and set into jewelry, a forceful blow may still chip or cleave the stone.

CROWN
The area of any faceted gemstone that is above the girdle.

FACET
A flat, polished surface on a cut diamond or other gemstone.

FANCY COLOR
The term used to describe any diamond with a body color that is so strong that the diamond is considered that color, rather than simply a colorless diamond with a slight yellow or brown tint. Fancy color diamonds include pink, red, orange, brown, yellow, olive, green, blue, purple, gray, black, and white (which is not the same as colorless).

FANCY CUT
The term used to describe any style of diamond cut other than round brilliant.

GIA
The Gemological Institute of America, a nonprofit, educational organization whose grading systems are used as standards throughout the jewelry industry.

GIRDLE
The outer edge of a cut stone and the area of the stone that is usually held by the prongs or the bezel. The girdle separates the stone's crown above from its pavilion below.

INCLUSION
Any internal *clarity characteristic in a diamond.*

LOUPE
A small magnifier that fits in the eye.

PAVILION
The facets of a cut gemstone that are below the girdle.

TABLE
The large facet on the top of a diamond or other gemstone.

10X
Ten-power magnification, the standard used for grading diamonds.

THE FIRST c:color

When most people think of diamonds, they conjure up an image of clear, colorless stones, so it is perhaps surprising to discover that diamonds actually come in almost every imaginable color.

Most diamonds range from colorless to light yellow or brown and can be graded using the color grading system developed by the Gemological Institute of America (GIA). This color grading scale begins at D (colorless) and runs through Z (light yellow or brown). Yellow or brown diamonds that have a color deeper than Z are called fancy colored diamonds.

They occur naturally in many vibrant ranges of color including pink, red, orange, brown, yellow, olive, green, blue, purple, gray, and even black. These colored diamonds are called "fancy" colored diamonds. Colorless diamonds, diamonds that show no hint of body color at all, are graded D, E, or F on the GIA color scale. When well cut, these fine white diamonds boast a dispersion (often referred to as "fire") that flashes with all the spectral colors of the rainbow.

Diamonds also occur in G through Z colors, although any stone graded below J will show a noticeable yellow or brownish body color.

The diamonds used for engagement rings, in wedding rings, in diamond earring and pendants, and as accent stones in gemstone jewelry are usually somewhere above K or L on the color scale.

The following chart explains the color differences within the D through Z diamond category, and should be helpful when evaluating the differences between several diamonds.

Bear in mind that compromises must often be made when purchasing a diamond and in many cases, a consumer will opt for a lower color in order to be able to purchase a larger stone at a desired price.

D E F	COLORLESS	*Stones in these grades will appear completely colorless and are referred to as 'fine white.' These are exceptional stones.*
G H I J	NEAR COLORLESS	*These stones will "face up" colorless: they will appear white to an untrained eye, although a trained eye may pick up slight traces of color.*
K L M	SLIGHT BODY TINT	*These stones will appear tinted yellow or brownish, especially when shown side by side with higher color stones. Smaller stones may, however, "face up" colorless.*
N O P Q R S T U W X Y Z	VERY LIGHT BODY TINT TO TINTED WITH COLOR	*These stones will show increasingly more body color, as we move through the range of color grades. After grade N, the yellow or brownish body color will be noticeable even to the untrained eye, especially when compared side-by-side with stones of higher color.* *"Off-white" diamonds (as these grades are often called), are much lower in price, and large stones can often be purchased relatively inexpensively.* *Grading as "Fancy Yellow" or "Fancy Brown" begins for diamonds that exceed the Z color grade.*

THE SECOND c:clarity

Diamonds are graded by their clarity, which describes the level of a diamond's purity—or the presence or absence of inclusions and blemishes.

It is easy to become confused when the terms used for evaluating a diamond's clarity are bandied about by people knowledgeable about diamond grading.

What do all those Vs and Ss mean anyway? Is a VVS better than a VS? And why do some diamonds also have numbers in their clarity grades? What's the difference between an SI-2 and an SI-1?

As with any field requiring training and expertise, the jargon used in the diamond business can be daunting, but it need not be incomprehensible. The following chart makes it fairly simple to understand what the various terms mean. Understanding clarity grades will help you put the range of diamond purity in a context that you can use when purchasing diamond jewelry.

GIA GRADE

F	FLAWLESS
	Completely free from all internal and external inclusions when examined by a trained grader using 10X magnification.
IF	INTERNALLY FLAWLESS
	No internal inclusions of any kind visible to a trained eye using 10X magnification.
VVS-I, VVS-2	VERY, VERY SLIGHTLY INCLUDED #I AND #2
	Very minute inclusions that are extremely difficult for a trained eye to locate using 10X magnification.
VS-I, VS-2	VERY SLIGHTLY INCLDED #I AND #2
	Minor inclusions that are difficult for a trained eye to locate using 10X magnification.
SI-I, SI-2	SLIGHTLY INCLUDED #I AND #2
	Noticeable inclusions that are easily visible to a trained eye using 10X magnification.
I-I, I-2, I-3	INCLUDED #I, #2, AND #3
	Obvious inclusions that range from somewhat to very easy to locate.

THE THIRD C:cut

SEVEN CLASSIC SHAPES

Cut is the most important of any diamond's Four Cs. A well-cut stone of any shape will increase the amount of light that is reflected within the stone and maximize its brilliance and beauty.

There are seven classic diamond cuts.

	ROUND BRILLIANT	A standard and popular style for diamonds and other gemstones. A round brilliant cut consists of fifty-seven or fifty-eight facets and was developed to maximize a diamond's brilliance and fire. Properly cut round brilliant diamonds have been cut to the optimal table, crown, and pavilion proportions for brilliancy. "Old Mine" diamonds are an early form of the round brilliant cut, distinguished by their cushion-shaped, almost square girdles.
	MARQUISE	A style of diamond cut that uses the facet shape and placement of the round brilliant style, but which results in a boat-shaped diamond that is pointed on each end.
	PEAR	A variation of the fifty-seven or fifty-eight facet round brilliant cut that results in a pear-shaped diamond with a rounded bottom and a pointed top. To obtain the pear shape, one or two facets may be eliminated resulting in a stone of fifty-six facets.
	OVAL	An elongated variation of the fifty-eight-facet brilliant cut that results in a rounded oblong stone.
	HEART	A variation of the fifty-eight-facet brilliant cut which results in a heart-shaped stone. The heart-shaped diamond is the most romantic of all the diamond shapes.
	EMERALD	A form of step cutting resulting in a rectangular-shaped stone—sometimes square— in which the facets both above and below the girdle are all four-sided and parallel to the girdle. A baguette is a small, rectangular diamond available in both tapered and straight forms, which sometimes uses fewer facets. Baguettes are most commonly used as accent stones in both diamond and colored gemstone jewelry.
	TRILLION	A variation of the fifty-eight-facet round brilliant cut that results in a triangular-shaped stone.

THE FOURTH C: carat

and how diamonds are sold by their weight

Diamonds are identified and sold by their carat weight. (Carat is *not* the same as karat, which refers to the purity of gold, as in fourteen-karat or eighteen-karat gold), although both words are derived from the Arabic word *qirat*, which means "bean pod". In Oriental bazaars, a carob seed was a unit of weight measurement.

Points are another unit of weight used to measure diamonds; one carat is equal to one hundred points. (Helpful Tip: To grasp the concept of one hundred points equaling one carat, think of one hundred pennies equaling one dollar, so a stone that weighs a quarter of a carat, weighs twenty-five points.)

Many people, including jewelers, refer to diamonds in rounded-off fractions, as in a quarter-carat, a half-carat, or a three-quarter-carat stone. These terms are sometimes used as handy shorthand for describing the general range of a diamond's size, but be aware that a diamond referred to as quarter-carat does not necessarily weigh precisely twenty-five points.

The following chart specifies a range of diamond weights that corresponds to fractions of carats used in the jewelry industry. Remember, that no matter how a ring or a diamond is described —"this wedding band has a third of a carat total weight of diamonds"—you should always be told the precise weight of each diamond or a minimum guaranteed weight or total weight of all diamonds—in carats—of the diamond or diamonds you are purchasing in a piece of jewelry.

WEIGHT RANGES TYPICALLY COVERED BY SIMPLE FRACTIONS

AVERAGE WEIGHT RANGE COVERED	FRACTION CT
0.90 CARAT THROUGH 0.95 CARAT	9/10 CARAT
0.84 CARAT THROUGH 0.89 CARAT	7/8 CARAT
0.70 CARAT THROUGH 0.83 CARAT	3/4 CARAT
0.57 CARAT THROUGH 0.69 CARAT	5/8 CARAT
0.47 CARAT THROUGH 0.56 CARAT	1/2 CARAT
0.38 CARAT THROUGH 0.46 CARAT	3/8 CARAT
0.30 CARAT THROUGH 0.37 CARAT	1/3 CARAT
0.23 CARAT THROUGH 0.29 CARAT	1/4 CARAT
0.18 CARAT THROUGH 0.22 CARAT	1/5 CARAT
0.15 CARAT THROUGH 0.17 CARAT	1/6 CARAT
0.12 CARAT THROUGH 0.14 CARAT	1/8 CARAT
0.90 CARAT THROUGH 0.11 CARAT	1/10 CARAT

15

YOU NEVER KNEW ABOUT DIAMONDS

things

1.

Every diamond is at least 990 million years old. Many diamonds are 3.2 billion years old.

2.

Diamonds were first discovered in India about 2,800 years ago.

3.

It is estimated that a total of only two hundred tons of diamonds have been mined since they were first discovered.

4.

Diamonds are formed between 62 and 124 miles beneath the surface of the earth.

5.

The word diamond comes from the Greek word *adamas*, which means "invincible".

6.

Ancient Greeks believed that diamonds were the tears of the gods.

7.

There is a legend that diamonds will keep away ghosts and prevent nightmares.

8.

The fourteenth century alchemist Pierre de Boniface claimed that diamonds could make a wearer invisible.

9.

Napoleon had a 140-carat diamond set in the hilt of his sword for good luck.

10.

Red diamonds are the rarest of the colored or fancy diamonds.

11.

Diamonds not only come in colors, they also occur in black. One of the most famous black diamonds is the 67.5-carat cushion-cut Black Orlov, which was named after Count Grigory Orlov, lover of the infamous Catherine the Great.

12.

The marquise cut of diamond was named for the French King Louis XV's mistress the Marquise de Pompadour.

13.

The Gemological Institute of America's twenty-three-letter (D through Z) diamond-color grading system was created in 1953. They skipped letters A, B, and C to distinguish their system from other diamond color grading systems in use at the time.

14.

The 45.52-carat blue Hope Diamond is the most famous gem in the world. It is the largest blue diamond in existence.

15.

According to ninth-century accounts, if a man broke off an engagement, his ex-fiancé got to keep the engagement ring. If the woman broke the engagement, she was obligated to return the ring.

Some ask'd how pearls

did grow, and where?

ROBERT HERRICK,

The Rock of Rubies and the Quarry of Pearls

pearl

beloved

Nature has blessed its many creatures with a wide range of ways to defend themselves. The glorious and beloved pearl, in all its delightful variations, is in fact a by-product of the natural defense system of several species of mollusks.

Pearls are made of an organic substance called nacre (aragonite). In order to protect their sensitive inner surfaces, certain types of mollusks, especially the bivalve oyster and the mussel, build up nacre around an irritant, such as a tiny parasite. Layer after layer of nacre accumulates until the object we know as a pearl is formed.

NATURAL pearls

Natural pearls occur when the irritant is accidental; for example, when a tiny sea creature or other foreign matter somehow ends up inside a mollusk. These types of pearls are a result of a completely natural interaction of the oyster and its environment; they are very rare and very expensive.

Natural pearls come in shades of white, cream, and—the rarest color—black. They are often irregular in shape and tend to be not as perfectly round as cultured pearls. There are many sources for natural pearls around the world, including the Red Sea, the Indian Ocean, and the Persian Gulf, although their cost prohibits their routine use in jewelry.

Cultured pearls come into being when man gives nature a little push. Cultured pearl farmers raise and protect mollusks and deliberately implant an irritant—a mother-of-pearl bead and a tiny piece of mollusk tissue, or sometimes just the tissue—inside a mollusk. The mollusk reacts to this "intruder" exactly as if the foreign object had been accidentally introduced into its body: it builds layer upon layer of nacre around the irritant until the growth resembles a natural pearl.

CULTURED pearls

Most people credit Kokichi Mikimoto with the perfection of the cultured pearl process, which he developed in Japan in the early twentieth century. The first attempt to culture pearls allegedly was made by the Arabs living by the Red Sea in the second century B.C., as recounted by the Greek Apollonius of Tyre (although many historians doubt these claims).

The largest producer of cultured pearls today is China. Japan is also a major supplier. Another important source of cultured pearls are the South Seas, including Polynesia and Australia.

Cultured pearls range in size from two millimeters to eight or nine millimeters, or even more. South Sea Pearls are typically 10 to 12 mm and can be as large as 20 mm.

Helpful Tip: There are twenty-five millimeters in an inch, which makes it simple to calculate how many pearls of a given size make up an inch. For example, five five-millimeter pearls make up one inch of pearls; while it takes eight three-millimeter pearls to equal an inch.

CULTURED pearls

Cultured pearls are graded
and evaluated by five factors:

LUSTER

SIZE

SHAPE

SURFACE

COLOR

Let's look at these characteristics
one at a time.

LUSTER

Luster refers to the way light reflects off the surface of a cultured pearl and is often described as its sheen. Cultured pearls range in quality from a very *high luster*—an intense, brilliant surface—to *low luster*—a dull, flat surface that has almost no reflection whatsoever. The luster of a high-quality strand of cultured pearls is one of its most appealing visual elements and is often the deciding factor when purchasing cultured pearls. There is nothing more dramatic than placing a high-luster strand of cultured pearls on black velvet right next to a same-size strand with very low luster. The contrast is striking and a dramatic illustration of the difference between cultured pearls of varying sheen.

Occasionally, fine cultured pearls with excellent luster also have *orient*. When light strikes the surface of a cultured pearl with orient, it is diffracted by the nacre which produces tiny subtle rings of rainbow colors.

SIZE

As previously discussed, cultured pearls most often occur in sizes from two to six millimeters in diameter. Fewer cultured pearls are seven to nine millimeters. Certain cultured pearls can be as large as ten or even twenty millimeters. Tiny cultured pearls from one to 1.75 millimeters in diameter are called seed pearls. As the size of cultured pearls goes up, so does the price. Lately, five- to six-millimeter cultured pearls have been extremely popular and affordably priced. "Half-drilled" cultured pearls are used in rings and earrings; "fully-drilled" cultured pearls are used for stringing on silk or nylon cord for necklaces and bracelets.

SHAPE

Cultured pearls grow in many shapes, including round, oval, pear, button, and other forms. For a traditional look, the perfectly round cultured pearls are the rarest, the most prized, and all other qualities being equal, the most valuable. Other shapes often lend themselves to interesting and appealing uses, such as in earrings, brooches, and free-form rings. Necklace strands of round cultured pearls (as closely matched in shape as possible) are classics, but today women can choose from creative contemporary designs that use a wide range of cultured pearl shapes.

SURFACE

This term refers to imperfections or blemishes that may occur on the surface of a cultured pearl. These include bumps, blisters, cracks, and spots. Better cultured pearls are free from large blemishes. When selecting a strand of cultured pearls, each cultured pearl should match as closely as possible the others on the strand. (Some blemishes can be effectively eliminated in cultured pearl strands by drilling the cultured pearl at the site of the imperfection, although this is not practical when the cultured pearls have many bumps or cracks.) As with other gemstones, the "cleaner" the surface, the more valuable the cultured pearl. However, tiny marks on cultured pearls are part of their basic nature. They should not be considered a detriment; they are, in fact, a hallmark of the cultured pearl's natural essence.

COLOR

Cultured pearls range from light to dark, in a wide spectrum of body colors and a variety of overtones. Light cultured pearls come in soft shades of pink, white, or cream. Dark cultured pearls include cultured pearls that are silver-gray to dark gray with overtones of dark blue, purple, blue-green, green, and bronze. Colored cultured pearls also come in light to medium shades of orange, yellow, green, blue, violet, purple, pink, and gray.

WHAT IS...

AKOYA PEARL

Akoyas are saltwater pearls harvested from Akoya oysters in Japan and China; most are cultured although extremely rare natural Akoyas do exist. Most have a white or cream body color. They can be slightly rosy; many are naturally pinkish; some are naturally pewter gray. They are round to roundish in shape, and they range from two to nine millimeters in size.

BAROQUE PEARL

A baroque pearl is a pearl that is irregular in shape. Baroque pearls are not symmetrical— they have a noticeably irregular shape. They can be cultured or natural pearls.

BLACK TAHITIAN PEARL

A black Tahitian is a dark pearl—natural or cultured—created, it is believed, by the type of plankton the oyster consumes as well as the specific species of oyster. Most are produced by the giant oyster Pinctada margaritifera.
Out of one hundred such oysters, five will yield high quality pearls, a further fifteen will yield saleable goods, and twenty will produce substandard pearls that will be rejected. The remaining sixty oysters will produce nothing. An important source for black cultured pearls today is French Polynesia, especially the waters around Tahiti—hence the name black Tahitian.

BLISTER PEARL

A blister pearl is a pearl that is formed while attached to the wall or inner shell of a mollusk. Blister pearls must be removed along with a part of the shell. They vary in size and shape and can be natural or cultured.

CIRCLE CULTURED PEARL OR RINGED PEARL

Circle cultured pearls are a relatively new type of baroque pearl that many pearl aficionados have compared to fancy Christmas-tree ornaments. A circle cultured pearl is a cultured freshwater or saltwater pearl that has concentric circles running around its diameter, producing an intriguing ribbed look. Recently, strands of ten-millimeter and larger circle cultured pearls have become very popular because of their unique and appealing look.

FRESHWATER CULTURED PEARL

Freshwater cultured pearls are grown in lakes and rivers, in the United States, Japan, and China. They come in several colors, including white, pink, lavender, peach, apricot, and beige. Some freshwater pearls look like grains of rice; some are ovalish; some are close to perfectly round.

MABE PEARLS

Mabes are half-pearls that are cultured against the inside shell of an oyster resulting in cultured pearls that usually have a domed shape. The outline of the pearl is commonly round or oval. Mabe pearls are then assembled onto a base.

MOTHER-OF-PEARL

Mother-of-pearl is the pearly internal layer of a mollusk shell. Mother-of-pearl is often used for decorative inlay and for watch dials.

SOUTH SEA PEARL

A South Sea pearl is a large saltwater pearl, cultured or natural, averaging from ten to twenty millimeters in size. Nearly all come from the oceans around Australia, Myanmar, Indonesia, and other South Pacific countries. South Sea pearls occur in round, oval, and baroque shapes. Their colors range from white and gold to pastel shades. The March 1999 issue of **Modern Jeweler** *(an industry magazine) said "The South Sea pearl is for the customer who wants something of great prestige and is willing to pay whatever it takes to get it." Golden South Sea cultured pearls from Australia are the rarest of all South Sea cultured pearls.*

PEARL LENGTHS AND SIZES

CHOKER	*Fifteen inches*
CHUTE	*Sixteen to eighteen inches*
COLLAR	*Sixteen inches, with a flat design*
DOG COLLAR	*Thirteen or fourteen inches, consisting of several rows of cultured pearls and worn very snug around the neck*
MATINEE LENGTH	*Twenty-two inches*
OPERA LENGTH	*Thirty inches*
PRINCESS LENGTH	*Twenty or twenty-one inches*
ROPE	*Forty inches or longer*
STANDARD (TRADITIONAL) LENGTH	*Eighteen inches*
TORSADE	*Several strands of cultured pearls (usually freshwater) twisted together into one strand. Sometimes different-colored strands are used in one torsade, providing a striking multicolored look.*
LARIAT	*A long strand with decorated ends that are tied or looped instead of clasped.*
EARRINGS	*Usually four to nine millimeters in diameter.*
UNIFORM	*A strand of pearls that appear to be all one size. The size of cultured pearls used for uniform strands may range from three millimeters to nine or even ten millimeters. Uniform strands actually need to have a slight size graduation of a half-millimeter in order to appear uniform.*
GRADUATED	*Graduated: A strand of cultured pearls with one large central pearl and progressively smaller pearls tapering down to each end.*

CARING FOR YOUR PEARLS

Pearl strands should be worn at least twice a month. The contact with your skin keeps the pearls moisturized and lustrous, and wearing them regularly keeps them falling naturally and gracefully. Wipe your pearls with a soft cloth after each wearing.

Pearls should be the last thing you put on and the first thing you take off. Hair spray, colognes, and makeup will damage pearl's organic nacre and will eventually ruin them.

Do not swim while wearing your pearls. Chlorine will damage the pearls themselves, and water will saturate and fray the bead cord on which they are strung.

Pearls should sit snugly up against one another with a small knot between each. With regular wear, knotted strands will loosen and you will begin to notice a space between the pearls and the knots. This is your cue to have them restrung. Depending on wear, a complete restringing every two to three years is wise. (Some experts recommend annual restringing, although in most cases it is not necessary.)

Pearl stud earrings can be washed gently with mild soap and water. Be sure to dry them thoroughly with a soft cloth.

Do not let your pearl jewelry rub up against your other jewelry.

Never place pearls in an ultrasonic cleaner and never have them steam-cleaned.

LEGEND AND LORE ABOUT PEARLS

Pearls represent purity, modesty, and gentleness. They are symbolic of the moon, and also signify hidden talents, sexual fulfillment, and the soul.

The word pearl comes from the Latin word *sphaerula* which means "sphere." Pearls were once believed to be the tears of the gods. The ancient Greeks believed that pearls were drops of moisture flung from Aphrodite's body as she emerged from the sea. Pearls were among the first natural objects to be valued by man. The pearl fisheries of the Persian Gulf are at least two thousand years old, and in China pearls were worn as adornment more than three thousand years ago. The largest pearl in the world is the Pearl of Asia, which weighs an astonishing 605 carats.

Cleopatra possessed two magnificent pear-shaped natural pearls. When Marc Antony questioned her love for him, she came up with a dramatic way of proving it: she dissolved one of her precious pearls in a goblet of wine which she then drank.

Jesus refers to pearls in his Sermon on the Mount. In Matthew 7:6, he says, "Give not that which is holy unto the dogs, neither cast ye your pearls before swine, lest they trample them under their feet..."

In 1917, Pierre Cartier paid for a New York mansion on Fifth Avenue with a double-strand pearl necklace. Today, that mansion is Cartier's world headquarters.

PEARL FASHION TIPS

Pearls are subtle, gracefully elegant, and they go with everything. They look lovely with suits and dresses. Pearls also add a stylish accent to sportswear, and even to jeans and a t-shirt. Many women consider a strand of pearls, a pair of pearl earrings, and a pearl ring to be three essential components of their basic jewelry wardrobes.

DARK-SKINNED WOMEN LOOK WONDERFUL IN PEARLS WITH A CREAM OR GOLD TINT.

PINK COMPLEXIONS ARE BEST COMPLEMENTED BY PEARLS WITH A CREAMY ROSE COLOR.

UNIFORM STRANDS ARE THE MOST POPULAR STYLE OF PEARL NECKLACE TODAY.

PEARL CHOKERS LOOK BEST ON LONG NECKS.

GRADUATED STRANDS LOOK BEST ON SHORTER OR WIDER NECKS.

PEARL EARRINGS WITH DIAMONDS CALL ATTENTION TO THE EYES AND HAIR.

A SINGLE STRAND OF PEARLS IS PERFECT FOR DAILY WEAR AT THE OFFICE; A MULTISTRAND NECKLACE IS THE ULTIMATE ACCESSORY FOR EVENING WEAR.

THE METALS

platinum

glorious

Put forth thy hand,

Reach at the glorious gold.

WILLIAM SHAKESPEARE,
Henry IV, part two

gold

Gold, which has been with us throughout history, has amazing properties that make it one of the most unique natural substances on earth. Gold is the world's most treasured metal.

Gold is often described as the supreme raw material. It is the only precious metal that combines irresistible beauty, remarkable workability, indestructibility, and rarity. Gold is so superlative that it has long been a symbol for all things good — we say that someone has a "Heart of Gold", or something is "Good as Gold", and perhaps most memorably, characterize the great commandment to love one's neighbor as "The Golden Rule".

Gold was the very first Christmas gift, along with frankincense and myrrh. The ancient Egyptians, who believed gold was solidified fire, fashioned it into gem-encrusted jewelry and priceless art objects. This precious metal also added glistening brilliance to the religious objects of the Incas.

The Asante people of Gold Coast western Africa so loved crafting their intricate gold jewelry, that they would periodically melt down their older pieces to create new ones. The Bible even mentions gold and refers to its value, both earthly and spiritual. The talent referred to in the Bible was actually a gold coin that weighed eight and one-half grams. In the Book of Matthew, Jesus tells the parable of the king who forgave a debt of ten thousand talents owed him by one of his servants. The debt and the king's generosity were significant; at today's retail prices, eighty-five thousand grams of fourteen-karat gold would be worth approximately two million dollars.

Amazingly, almost all the gold mined in the last six thousand years is still in the possession of man. If all of this gold were shaped into a cube, it would measure only sixty feet on each side and would fit neatly beneath the Eiffel Tower—and be worth a trillion dollars. There is a legend that a tiny part of Cleopatra's crown is in every single piece of gold jewelry in existence today, and that the piece of jewelry you wear today may also contain gold from an Egyptian tomb or from King Solomon's temple.

In the last 6,000 years, over 125,000 tons of gold have been mined. The accumulation of this total falls into two categories: before the California Gold Rush of 1848 and after the California Gold Rush. It is estimated that only about 10,000 tons of gold had been mined before 1848. This means that approximately ninety-two percent of the world's gold has been produced in the past 150 years. In the past decade alone, over 2,000 tons of gold have been made into jewelry each year. Pure gold is twenty-four karat (24K) and is very soft. One ounce of pure gold can be stretched into a wire an astonishing five miles long or hammered into a sheet that could cover an area of 100 square feet—it would be so thin that light would pass through it.

In addition to its use in jewelry, gold is also used as currency and is used in medicine, dentistry, the aerospace industry, and the electronics industry.

TRUE colors

Other metals, called alloys, are added to pure gold to make it stronger and easier to work with. Alloys can also change gold's color. Natural yellow gold can be alloyed to create white gold, pink gold, and green gold, among others. Many manufacturers consider their special alloy combinations proprietary information.

GOLD COLOR	ALLOYS ADDED TO PURE 24K GOLD TO ACHIEVE DESIRED COLORS	INTERESTING FACTS
YELLOW GOLD	Copper and silver	*Yellow gold comprises eighty-five percent of the gold sold throughout the world.*
WHITE GOLD	Nickel, zinc, silver, platinum, and palladium	*White gold symbolizes friendship and is the most important of the colored golds.*
PINK (ROSE) GOLD	Copper	*Pink gold has become increasingly popular and looks lovely when combined with yellow or green gold*
GREEN GOLD	Silver, copper, and zinc	*Green gold is being used more and more frequently with pink gold and yellow gold; it is an important part of Black Hills gold's signature grape-leaf design.*

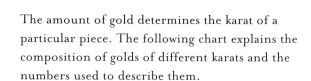

GOLD karat

The amount of gold determines the karat of a particular piece. The following chart explains the composition of golds of different karats and the numbers used to describe them.

AMERICAN KARAT MARKING	PERCENTAGE OF PURE GOLD	UNIVERSAL MARKING	INTERESTING FACTS
8	33.3%	333	This is the minimum karat that can be called "gold" in Mexico.
9	37.5%	375	This is a very popular gold in Ireland and the United Kingdom; it is also the minimum karat that can be called "gold" in Canada and the United Kingdom.
10	41.7%	417	This is the minimum karat that can be called "gold" in the United States.
12	50%	500	12K gold has not been widely made since 1932 when the 14K standard was set, although Black Hill's gold is manufactured in 12K.
14	58.5%	585	14K is the most popular gold sold in the United States.
15	62.5%	625	15K has not been made since 1932 when the 14K standard was set.
18	75%	750	18K is the most popular gold sold in Italy and other European countries.
19.2	80%	800	19.2K is a popular gold in Portugal.
20	83.3%	833	This is a very high-karat gold notable for its bright yellow color.
22	91.6%	916	This is another very high-karat gold that is popular in Asia and the Middle East; it is very soft due to the small proportion of strengthening alloys.
23.76	99%	990	This is ninety-nine percent pure gold and is popular in Hong Kong, China, and elsewhere in Asia.
24	100%	1000	This is pure gold, with no alloys added. Jewelry is made using 24K gold in Turkey, India, and Asia, but it is very soft, somewhat brassy in color, and more expensive than other golds.

RINGS AND CHAINS OF gold

Gold is a popular medium for jewelry. The United States is the world's largest market for gold jewelry and the variety of styles and themes available offers something for everyone's taste. Favored types of gold jewelry, in order of sales, are neckchains, earrings, charms, chain and bangle bracelets, and rings, including wedding rings. It is believed that the ancient Egyptians were one of the first—if not the very first—to use a solid gold band

as a wedding ring five thousand years ago, believing the endless circle symbolized the eternity of marriage. Today, more than nineteen tons of gold are made into wedding rings each year.

For centuries, the gold chain has been a signature jewelry item spanning time and civilizations. Gold neckchains, which were worn as early as the seventh century B.C., are now the most popular way to wear gold. Today, women favor rope, link, box, snake, bead, omega, mesh, stampato, and San Marco chains; men like rope, link, figaro, Cuban, and mariner chains. A gold chain is a symbol of love: placing a chain around the neck of a loved one links that person to you.

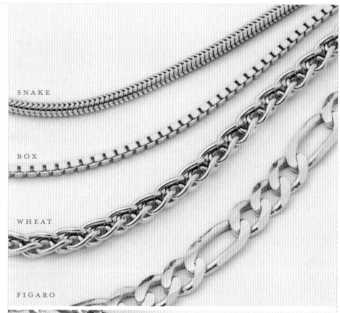

SNAKE

BOX

WHEAT

FIGARO

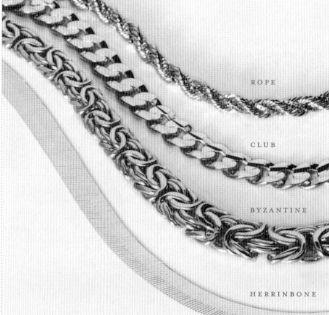

ROPE

CLUB

BYZANTINE

HERRINBONE

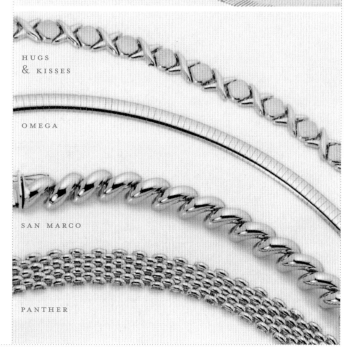

HUGS & KISSES

OMEGA

SAN MARCO

PANTHER

THE ITALIAN tradition

From couture fashions to fast cars to sleek furniture, the Italian design aesthetic is unrivaled in its ability to intrigue us. And nowhere else is the Italian appreciation of beauty more evident than in their magnificent fine-jewelry designs.

Jennifer Leventhal,
JQ Magazine, April/May 1999

Italy is the world's indisputable leader in gold jewelry manufacturing. The Italian jewelry industry is at least three thousand years old. In fact, wealthy Italian patrons during the Renaissance encouraged goldsmiths much the way they sponsored artists, sculptors, and musicians. Today, Italy uses more than four hundred tons of gold a year to make the gorgeous Italian jewelry renowned and beloved around the world— an incredible three-quarters of Italy's jewelry output is exported. Italian gold is associated with quality and antiquity, in perfect balance with cutting-edge technology and innovative design.

WHAT QUALITY MEANS

The following factors all contribute to the overall quality of each piece of gold jewelry and should be carefully considered before any purchase is made:

SUPERIOR CRAFTSMANSHIP AND DESIGN

THE FINEST QUALITY MATERIALS

AN APPEALING OVERALL STYLE

EXCELLENT FINISH AND TEXTURE

SUPERIOR STRUCTURAL INTEGRITY

STRICT KARAT STANDARDS

EXCELLENT POLISH AND PERFECT LEVELNESS OF STONES IN GEM-SET GOLD

A DISPLAY OF THE QUALITY MARK OR HALLMARK

FREEDOM FROM CASTING DEFECTS

stunning

Silver is known as "The Queen of Metals" and is so special that a litany of superlatives is needed to do it justice. Of the three precious metals, gold and platinum being the other two, silver is the most abundant, the most lustrous, the most reflective, the least expensive, the whitest of the white metals, the easiest to work with, and the very first of the precious metals to be used to make jewelry.

Silver was in use in Egypt over 5,500 years ago and silver headbands from prehistoric times have been found in Spain. There are many references to silver in the Bible; one of the most notable is found in Psalms 12:6: (The words of the Lord are pure words, as silver tried in a furnace of earth, purified seven times.) But for all its popularity as jewelry, silver's most important use historically and today, is as monetary currency.

In its purest form, silver is called metallic, free, or native. Sterling silver is alloyed. Pure silver, as it comes from the mine, is gray in color and too soft for practical use. Native silver is made into sterling silver by adding alloys, usually copper, nickel, and zinc. The alloys harden the silver and give it its characteristic silvery color. Silver is the easiest metal to work with, because it is so versatile. It is silver's malleability that makes it so easy to shape. It can be hammered so thin that light shines through it. Silver is the most reflective of all metals; however, it also scratches easily. Pure silver is harder than pure gold, but softer than copper. It is the whitest of metals. The leading producers of silver are the United States, Mexico, Canada, Peru, Russia, and Australia. Each year in the United States more than six million troy ounces of silver are made into jewelry.

HOW STERLING SILVER GOT ITS NAME

Sterling silver is ninety-two and one-half percent silver and seven and one-half percent alloy. For decades, German silversmiths refined silver for the English, adding alloys to pure silver to make a stronger, brighter metal, which was then used in England to make tableware, drinking vessels, and of course, jewelry. The English called the Germans "Easterlings" because they lived to the east. German silver became known as Easterling silver. Eventually the "ea" was dropped and the metal became known simply as sterling silver. The Germans' recipe for sterling silver survives to this day.

A SHINING STAR

Silver jewelry is popular around the world. Women in Egypt and India favor silver anklets; Hindu women wear silver bangles and silver toe rings; Native American silver jewelry is enormously popular. Silver is a wonderfully appealing, luminous metal that is both affordable and precious. It lends itself particularly well to innovative design and experimentation. Although the world's supply of silver is gigantic, silver is a by-product of mining gold. When gold mining diminishes, the supply of available silver also diminishes.

Silver goes perfectly with casual fashion styles but is versatile enough to also work beautifully with dressy and more formal styles. Historically, earrings have been the best-selling category of silver jewelry, but recently silver chains have been gaining, closely followed by necklaces and pendants. Silver bracelets with or without stone accents are a perennial favorite. Other popular silver jewelry styles include bands and big rings with faceted stones in colors from pastels to the deeper hues.

Silver is available in shiny and satin finishes. In some designs silver is combined with fourteen- or eighteen-karat yellow gold, creating a striking two-tone effect.

SILVER LININGS

Silver is associated with the moon, psychic energy, and purity. Silver also symbolizes peace, sincerity, chastity, eloquence, joy, and knowledge. The twenty-fifth wedding anniversary is known as the silver anniversary.

precious

platinum

Platinum has long been called the most precious of metals because of its rare and special qualities – characteristics not found in either gold or silver.

Platinum was used in Ecuador and Colombia before the fifteenth century. The Spaniards found large deposits of platinum in South America in 1750. By the 1920s, two-thirds of all the platinum mined was being used in the United States. Platinum is one of the heaviest and densest substances known to man. If the identical piece of jewelry were made in silver and platinum, the platinum piece would weigh twice as much as the silver piece. Platinum is also the hardest of the three precious metals and is three times as durable as gold.

In addition to its popularity for jewelry—it's beautiful, durable, and completely hypoallergenic—platinum's resistance to heat, rust, tarnish, and corrosion makes it perfect for use in cardiac pacemakers, heat- and chemical-resistant laboratory containers and automobile catalytic converters.

Eight tons of ore must be mined to produce one ounce of platinum. It takes three tons of ore to obtain one ounce of gold. Less than 158 tons of platinum are produced each year worldwide, compared to 1,500 tons of gold.

Platinum is mined in Russia, Colombia, South Africa, Canada, and Montana in the United States. Platinum mining is extremely labor intensive. It takes a full five months to process ore for pure platinum. Gold takes about a month. In addition, the polishing process for platinum takes far longer and requires more steps than the same process for gold.

UNITED STATES

PT

PLAT

PT950

950PT

950PLAT

These marks indicate 950 parts per thousand pure platinum.

Platinum jewelry in the United States can range from ninety-five percent to lesser percentages of pure platinum. Other metals from the platinum group, like iridium or ruthenium, are often used as alloys.

PT900

900PT

900PLAT

IRIDPLAT

10%IRIDPLATINUM

These marks signify 900 parts per thousand pure platinum.

EUROPE

950

This mark indicates ninety-five percent purity and is used to identify the highest quality platinum.

Elsewhere in the world it is possible to find platinum
at eighty-five percent (850 parts per thousand)
and even fifty-eight and a half percent (585 parts per thousand),
but they are not often found in the United States.

PLATINUM:
THE "HOT" METAL

*A dozen years ago, if you wanted
platinum jewelry, you would have
had a hard time finding it. Now, it
is sold in more than 15,000 retail
establishments in the U.S. alone.
In fact, since 1990, U.S.
consumer demand for platinum
jewelry has increased by 600%.
You can hardly watch a television
show or movie, or open a fashion
or lifestyle magazine, without
seeing someone famous wearing
platinum. It's a metal that your
grandmother and great-grand-
mother associated with fine
jewelry and diamonds. When
the government declared it a
strategic metal during WWII,
platinum disappeared from
jewelry stores. But in the late
1990s, as white metals became
the hottest jewelry trend, platinum
emerged as the perfect metal for
the new millennium.*

Platinum has been used for jewelry since the turn of the twentieth century, although the use of platinum for jewelry completely stopped during World War II. Platinum was declared a strategic metal by the United States government, and all of the platinum produced was used for electrical contacts, heat-resistant equipment, dentistry, and corrosion-proof wire. Even actress Mae West joined the war effort and sold her diamond and platinum jewelry.

Platinum is the purest and rarest of the white metals and is associated with luxury and elegance, although even jewelry lovers on a modest budget can wear platinum. There are many affordable platinum pieces such as polished crosses, bracelets, and pendants. Platinum is increasingly chosen for diamond engagement rings and wedding bands, and platinum watches have become popular (especially among men) for those who want a unique and special timepiece. Another very popular contemporary style is the combination of platinum and eighteen-karat yellow gold, in a sleek and elegant two-tone piece.

The platinum and diamond bow brooch (originally popularized in the early twentieth century) is back in fashion again as a stunning accessory for both daytime wear with suits and evening wear with dresses and gowns. In Japan, ninety-eight percent of all weddings and engagements involve a platinum ring. In the United States, platinum is a commemorative metal for the twentieth wedding anniversary. In Italy, platinum has been designated as the gift to give on the eighteenth birthday: since the eighteenth birthday is unquestionably a milestone, the Italians have decided that only platinum will do for such a momentous event.

FOR THE EXCEPTIONAL PERSON

Platinum is an exceptional product of nature, and jewelry made from this glorious metal is equally notable. Platinum is for the jewelry lover who wants a sleek, cool, classic look. When highly polished, platinum can be as reflective as a mirror; when buffed to a satin finish, it has a soft, silky look and feel. Platinum is the essence of subtle style, and no precious metal brings out the brilliance of diamonds the way platinum does.

care

There are so many different kinds of jewelry available today—the variety of shapes, sizes, colors, materials, and finishes seem endless. One might think that all of these different kinds of jewelry require different care but there are simple measures that will preserve the beauty of all jewelry from precious gemstones to faux pearls, and eighteen karat gold to sterling silver. The most effective way to preserve jewelry is by keeping it out of harm's way. It is virtually impossible to shield jewelry from the daily hustle and bustle of life and still relax and enjoy wearing it. But as the following points reveal, jewelry can be kept beautiful just by limiting its exposure to certain conditions.

PROTECTION

Hairspray, mousse, body lotion, moisturizer, perfume, make-up, shaving cream, soap, and other products may contain chemicals that are harmful to jewelry. These chemicals can leave a residue on jewelry, creating a dull film that is very difficult to remove. To prevent this buildup jewelry should be removed before bathing and grooming, and put on as the finishing touch. This extra step will reduce the need to clean jewelry.

Jewelry should also be removed before cleaning the kitchen, repairing a bike, or starting home improvement projects or any other work around around the house. Harsh, abrasive household cleaners can cause hard-to-remove build-up and leave dulling scratches. It is especially important to remove all jewelry when working with power tools: chains, rings, and earrings may get caught on a power tool and break or cause serious injury. (Be sure to follow all instructions when using such tools.)

Chlorine bleach can destroy jewelry, especially silver. When silver is exposed to chlorine bleach, the chemical has an oxidizing effect on the metal, causing the metal to turn an unsightly black. In most cases, standard household jewelry cleaners cannot remove the blackened metal. A professional jeweler with the proper equipment might be able to help. Jewelry should always be removed before working with chlorine bleach.

Although water is used to clean most jewelry, it must be thoroughly dry after exposure to water, especially before storing it in an enclosed space such as a self-sealing plastic bag or container. Moisture fosters tarnish on silver and can weaken springs and clasps. Moreover, certain jewelry and gemstones should never be soaked in water or worn when bathing (see page 152).

A sweltering sun or cold winter day should not harm jewelry. However, it is a good idea to keep jewelry away from extreme heat and cold. Some jewelry is more sensitive to heat than others. For example, extreme heat (comparable to the temperature of boiling water or very hot tap water) could damage jeweler's cement commonly used with costume jewelry, cultured pearls, or marcasite. Moreover, a rapid increase in temperature could cause thermal shock, leading to fractures in some gemstones.

STORAGE

The key to protecting jewelry is proper storage— each piece needs its own space. Metal can scratch or scuff other metal. Diamonds and other hard gemstones that come in contact with metal or each other can destroy luster or cause more serious damage. Each piece should be stored in its own individual container or compartment or in a pouch or a self-sealing plastic bag inside a large jewelry box. Bracelets and necklaces should be stored with the clasp fastened to prevent tangling.

cleaning

It is satisfying to watch your cherished items turn from dull and drab to shiny and bright and it takes just a few easy steps to restore such brilliance and luster. This section provides simple methods that will help clean your jewelry as effectively and as safely as possible. Certain methods are ideal for some jewelry but can cause damage to others that require extra-special care (see page 152).

MATERIALS

A clean bowl

Lukewarm water

Mild dishwashing liquid or a mild jewelry cleaning solution

Fine mesh plastic or stainless steel strainer *(for items with gemstones)*

Very soft, clean, dry cloth *(any dust or dirt on the cloth may scratch the piece)*

Small, soft bristled toothbrush or brush

Toothpick

A word about jewelry cleaners:
If you are using a commercial jewelry cleaner, always follow the directions for that particular cleaning product. It is also very important to maintain the freshness of the cleaner by storing it in a tightly-sealed container. A stale or contaminated cleaner may be ineffective or even damage your jewelry. Check to see if your jewelry cleaner indicates a shelf-life or expiration date.

PREPARATION

For older items with gemstones, check each setting to make sure that the stone is secure. Dirt and residue can fool you and act as a "cement," keeping the stone in place even if the setting has been rendered weak from wear. If this is the case, and the residue is removed when cleaning, the loose stone may fall out.

If working over or near a sink, plug the drain.

CLEANING *gold, silver, platinum, and most gemstones*

If using a mild jewelry cleaning solution, pour the solution into a clean bowl. You can also make your own solution by combining lukewarm water and mild dishwashing liquid (two tablespoons of dishwashing liquid to one quart of water.)

For items with gemstones, place the piece in a strainer and sit the strainer on top of the bowl so that the solution comes through the strainer and completely surrounds the piece. (The strainer will catch any stones that might possibly fall out.) For other items, simply place the piece in the bowl

Soak the item for ten to twenty minutes. (It is important to soak the piece long enough to soften and loosen any residue and dirt.)

For items with gemstones, remove the strainer to a large towel and inspect your jewelry to make sure that all the stones are in place.

Thoroughly, but gently, brush the top, sides, and bottom of the piece with a soft brush to remove the softened residue. For gemstones, you should also brush the underside of the stone. Use a toothpick to reach crevices and other hard-to-reach areas.

Rinse with clean water.

Thoroughly dry with a cloth that is soft, dry, and clean. If you are to store the piece immediately after cleaning, you should leave the piece on a towel in a safe place for an extended period of time to ensure that it is completely dry.

If the entire residue has not been removed, repeat the above steps as needed.

SPECIAL CLEANING

Some gemstones and types of jewelry have special cleaning needs; consult this chart to ensure the appropriate care for your jewelry.

SUITABLE FOR	CLEANING INSTRUCTIONS	SPECIAL CARE INSTRUCTIONS
AMBER	*Splash sparingly with a mixture of mild liquid soap and cool water (one teaspoon of soap to one cup of water).* *Rinse quickly with clean, cool water. (If rinsing in a sink, be sure the drain is plugged!)*	Don't use hot water, a steamer or an ultrasonic cleaner. Don't soak in water. Don't expose to extreme heat.
LAPIS LAZULI	*Dry with a soft, clean, absorbent cloth. Leave the piece on a towel for an extended period of time to ensure it is completely dry.*	Don't use hot water, a steamer or an ultrasonic cleaner. Don't soak in water.
CLOSED-BACK SETTINGS Any item with a closed-back setting requires special care because water can get trapped under the setting, making it very difficult to thoroughly dry.	*Wipe gently with a damp cloth that is soft and clean.* *Dry with a soft, clean, absorbent cloth.*	Don't use hot water, a steamer or an ultrasonic cleaner. Don't soak in water.
CORAL	*Leave the piece on a towel for an extended period of time to ensure it is completely dry.*	Don't use hot water, a steamer or an ultrasonic cleaner. Don't soak in water. Don't expose to cleaning agents or chemicals.
FASHION AND DESIGNER JEWELRY Costume/fashion jewelry can be versatile, with designs that allow you to wear your jewelry for any occasion. However, because jeweler's cement is often used to create those designs, it is important that you take special precautions when cleaning your costume/fashion jewelry.		Don't use hot water, a steamer or an ultrasonic cleaner. Don't soak in water. Don't expose to cleaning agents or other chemicals. Don't expose to extreme heat.
JADE		Don't use hot water, a steamer or an ultrasonic cleaner. Don't soak in water. Don't expose to cleaning agents or other chemicals.
MARCASITE Marcasite is often secured in a setting with jeweler's cement. This feature requires special cleaning.		Don't use hot water, a steamer or an ultrasonic cleaner. Don't soak in water. Don't expose to cleaning agents or other chemicals. Don't expose to extreme heat.
TURQUOISE		Don't use hot water, a steamer or an ultrasonic cleaner. Don't soak in water. Don't expose to cleaning agents or other chemicals.

SUITABLE FOR	CLEANING INSTRUCTIONS	SPECIAL CARE INSTRUCTIONS
CULTURED PEARL MABÉ PEARL MOTHER-OF-PEARL SHELL	*After wearing, wipe gently with a damp cloth that is soft and clean in order to remove any perspiration or oil that may have come from the skin, or any other residue.* *For regular cleaning, wipe gently with a damp cloth that is soft and clean.* *If you would like to use a cleaning agent, use a mild one that is specifically made for pearl products.* *Dry with a soft, clean, absorbent cloth. Leave the piece on a towel for an extended period of time to ensure it is completely dry.*	Don't use hot water, a steamer or an ultrasonic cleaner. Don't soak in water. Don't expose to hairspray or any other chemical (unless it is meant for pearl products). Don't expose to extreme heat.
EMERALD Although this gemstone is durable, its unique internal characteristics require extra-special care.	*Use the soaking and brushing method recommended on page 151. However, use cool water instead of lukewarm water. Also, instead of soaking for ten to twenty minutes, soak briefly for no more than five minutes.*	Don't use hot water, a steamer or an ultrasonic cleaner. Don't expose to heavy pressure. Don't expose to extreme heat. Don't expose to harsh or concentrated cleaning solutions. If using a mild cleaning solution, always dilute in water.
OPAL		Don't use hot water, a steamer or an ultrasonic cleaner. Don't expose to extreme heat.
OXIDIZED JEWELRY	*Unless the jewelry is in a closed-back setting, use the soaking method recommended on page 151. However, do not brush.* *If the entire surface of the piece is intentionally accented with oxidization, do not use any tarnish-remover product on the piece (e.g., silver polish, paste, or dip). Tarnish-remover could remove the accented finish. If the piece is only partially accented, you can use tarnish-remover on the unaccented areas. However, make sure that the tarnish-remover does not come in contact with any accented finish. For more control when applying tarnish-remover, use a cotton swab.*	Don't use hot water, a steamer or an ultrasonic cleaner.

gemstone TREATMENT AND ENHANCEMENT

INTRODUCTION

Treatment or enhancement. What's in a word? The distinction and relationship between these two terms is relatively straightforward. Simply put, treatment is the process and enhancement is the goal. Whether or not the goal is achieved is another question. A gemstone might be subjected to a treatment process, but it may come out unimproved or even in worse condition than it was before the treatment. If a gemstone has undergone treatment successfully, then it can be said to be enhanced. In other words, while all gem materials that have been put through a treatment process have been treated, not all of them have been enhanced. When it comes to the required disclosure during a sales presentation, this distinction works well for the jeweler. Enhancement is a much more positive-sounding term than treatment is.

Gemstone treatment is as old as the lapidary arts. As long as gemstones have been fashioned for ornamental purposes and personal adornment, stones of lesser quality have been treated in an attempt to enhance their appearance.

Today, many different treatment processes are used to enhance gem materials. Treatments are performed not only to enhance the outward appearance of gemstones, but in some instances to improve their lapidary properties and to imitate other gems. For example, porous massive calcite has been dyed pinkish orange to imitate coral and blue to imitate lapis lazuli, while cat's-eye tourmaline rough will sometimes be treated with epoxy to fill surface-reaching cracks and growth tubes prior to lapidary treatment. This process prevents cutting debris from being forced into the gem openings during shaping and polishing. This latter form of treatment also has the added benefit of reducing the visibility of any large, air-filled voids, thereby enhancing the appearance of the tourmaline.

Gemstone treatment has become increasingly sophisticated. While some of the earliest treatment processes employed heating in air, or wetting porous stones with oil or water to intensify their color, more recent techniques include irradiation-induced color enhancement, high-temperature glass surface-coating, and fracture-infilling, among others. The primary objective in perfecting such techniques has always been the same: to compensate for perceived natural defects and to increase the apparent value of the gemstone. The driving force behind treatment is making a material appear more desirable and thus more marketable. Historically, the rare and more costly natural gems have always inspired imitation.

Separating natural gems from those that have been enhanced can be difficult, and in some instances not economically feasible, particularly when modern treatments such as irradiation are employed. When testing a gemstone, a gemologist must avoid using any potentially destructive analyses. Fortunately, use of a gemological microscope can resolve internal and surface features that provide information that not only helps to identify the material but also to reveal the presence of an enhancement or an intentional alteration.

The microscope, however, cannot always conclusively detect enhancement. Proving the existence of a particular type of treatment, which microscopic examination or the general appearance of the stone may suggest, is not easily done. For example, the blue to violet color of a tanzanite strongly suggests that the stone has been heated. In fact, it is fair to assume that any tanzanite has been heat treated to gain its color, but conclusively proving it is beyond the scope of modern gemological practice.

The economics of gem enhancement detection must always be weighed against the potential value of the material to be tested. Take, for example, black chalcedony. While it is well known that the vast majority of such stones are treated to produce the black body color, proving it would cost far more than the value of the stone itself.

In this chapter an overview of the most commonly encountered treatment methods used for gemstone enhancement are described. It is important to remember that virtually any gemstone can be treated or even retreated at any point in time in an attempt to improve or enhance its appearance. The systematic study of gemstone treatment processes, and the visual clues to enhancement resulting from such treatments, is becoming so specialized and complex, that it merits its own subspecialty within the field of gemology.

GEMSTONE TREATMENT PROCESSES

The gemstone treatment processes listed blow are all currently in use. Some methods, such as the heat treatment of sapphires, the irradiation of diamonds, and the "oiling" of emeralds are very common and the disclosure of these enhancements is a vigorously debated issue in the trade. Other stable forms of enhancement, however, are so common that they have gained acceptance: The heat treatment of brown zoisite to create tanzanite, the irradiation of tourmaline to produce rubellite, or the dyeing of chalcedony to produce so-called black onyx. Some treatment processes are also used in combination, or in sequence, to obtain a particular result. This form of multiple processing is used in the production of bleached and plastic-impregnated jadeite jade and in the manufacture of quench-crackled and dyed rock crystal quartz.

Assembling
There are a wide variety of assembled stones that have been produced over the centuries. Almost any solid material can be cemented or fused to any other to produce an assembled stone. Sometimes this is done to add durability to a less durable gem material, like opal. Assembly may also be done to simulate natural gems, such as green garnet and glass doublets, an assemblage used to simulate natural emerald. The possibilities are almost limitless and are dictated only by the potential marketability and usefulness of the final product. Three of the most common assemblages are the garnet and glass doublet, the opal doublet, and the opal triplet.

Metal foils are used to back transparent to translucent gem materials to improve light reflectance. Even though this technique is centuries old, foil-backing is still a relatively popular form of enhancement. Generally, foil-backed stones are discernable with careful examination, but some assembled stones, including foil-backed ones, may be difficult to detect, especially in a closed setting.

Bleaching
This treatment desaturates a gem material's natural color. Chemical bleaching employs the use of such agents as hydrogen peroxide or acid to lighten or change a stone's color. Fading is a bleaching process that makes use of intentional exposure to light. Heat bleaching is frequently used to lighten amethysts that are too dark. Bleaching in acid is used to clean debris from the minute surface cracks in jadeite jade to prepare it for plastic impregnation, and to remove iron stains from crystal surfaces or surface-reaching cracks. Bleaching is also a relatively common process applied to cultured pearls to remove yellow or brown stains caused by the presence of undesirable organic compounds.

Cavity, Cleavage and Fracture Infilling
This process consists of the infilling of surface cavities or pits, or any similar depression, in a stone's surface. Cavity filling and cleavage or fracture infilling use some of the same materials, which include epoxy, plastic, or even wax, among others. Heat-

resistant, durable gem materials such as corundum may be cavity-filled with glass.

Chemical Staining

The use of reactive compounds, such as sugar and sulfuric acid, to produce a black carbon residue in gem materials (porous opal and chalcedony, for example) is categorized as chemical staining. Chemical staining imparts better color to a poor-quality, porous or fractured gem material. Induced iron stains in surface-reaching cracks may produce a pleasing color contrast, as well as make a synthetic look more natural. Silver salts can be precipitated in pearls to produce an artificial blackening, creating the visual impression of a natural black pearl. Just as with sugar and acid treatment, the smoke treatment of low-quality porous opals can produce a somewhat convincing substitute for black opal.

Coating

This is a method by which the surface color of a gem material is either slightly or completely altered in an effort to increase the gem material's apparent value. The application of a thin to extremely thin layer of transparent-to-opaque material to a stone's surface creates a new color, improves or masks an existing color, or even produces iridescent effects. Commonly used coatings include paint, fired enamel, ink, lacquer, stain, or a sputtered thin-film of a metallic oxide or metal. Some coatings enhance a gemstone's luster. Caution is advised when examining any seemingly coated gemstone, as not all coatings are intentional. Age, weathering, or accidental exposure to certain chemicals can produce an unintentional coating.

Dyeing

The intentional dyeing of a gem material is defined as the absorption of a coloring agent by a porous or fractured stone for the purpose of imparting a new color, enhancing an existing color, or obtaining a more uniform color. The coloring agents used as dyes are commonly colored oils or organic-based dyes. As an added benefit, these compounds often have refractive indices close to that of the host material. The starting materials are often

porous or fractured poor-quality gem materials such as low-end turquoise, or quench-crackled rock crystal quartz.

Heating

Heat treatment is one of the oldest, and one of the most common, forms of gemstone enhancement. It is most often used to alter an existing color, or to produce a color where none existed. Heat treatment may require very high temperatures to effect a change, as in the case of corundum, in which temperatures exceed 1500°C. Because heat treatment utilizes the gem's existing chemistry, no additional chemicals are used. Heat treatment may cause fluid inclusions within a gemstone to burst, resulting in damage to the surrounding area. The general appearance and condition of the mineral and fluid inclusions and the surrounding host may indicate if high-temperature heat treatment has been employed. Some mineral inclusions in sapphire (such as rutile, hematite and ilmenite) may impart a body-color to their host during high-temperature heat treatment. When this occurs, the inclusions are absorbed, or partially absorbed, by the host sapphire for the color-producing elements they contain. If the inclusions are not completely absorbed, the result is a zone of intensely colored sapphire surrounding what remains of the original inclusions.

Impregnation

This is the infusion of a usually permanent, color-less material like a plastic, or a semi-permanent organic agent such as wax, into a porous gem material. The purpose is to brighten the color, increase durability, increase translucency, or mask cracks and voids. Impregnation has been used on bleached jadeite, lapis lazuli, malachite, porous opal and turquoise, among others.

Irradiation

This treatment employs the use of electromagnetic waves, or high energy particles, to alter a gem material's color. During irradiation, neutrons, X-rays, electrons, ultraviolet light, or gamma rays may produce a new color in a gemstone, or change or improve a pre-existing color. Unless the irradiation has produced a distinctive pattern in the treated stone, the use of irradiation to improve a gemstone's color can be difficult to detect gemologically.

Laser Drilling

This process employs a high-energy coherent laser light to vaporize a hole into a gem, usually a diamond, to reach dark inclusions and alter their appearance, making them less visible. With diamonds, once the target inclusion has been reached and exposed to the surface by the laser, it is removed through the drill hole by the application of boiling acid.

Oiling

Through capillary action, an essentially colorless oil penetrates the surface-reaching fractures, cleavages, or fine pores of a gem material to replace air and hide these defects. Although relatively common, oiling is not a permanent form of enhancement and the practice is one of concern to the gem and jewelry trade today. Various more durable epoxy resins and mixtures are becoming increasingly popular for "oiling" emeralds and other gemstones. Traditional non-hardening oils, such as cedarwood oil, and the newer synthetic called palm oil or "palma," are also in widespread use.

Quench-Crackling

The objective of this treatment is to produce fine cracks in a gem material by first heating it to a relatively high temperature and then quenching it in a cold water or dye bath. The rapid and extreme temperature change creates tremendous thermal strain, which is relieved by the formation of numerous cracks through thermal shock. Quench-crackling makes inexpensive synthetic materials appear more natural, and allows natural transparent, single crystal (non-porous) gems, such as rock crystal quartz, to be dyed or chemically stained. As the dye penetrates the cracks, the fractures become less visible and the dye imparts its color to the stone.

Repair and Reconstruction

These two similar forms of treatment involve the production of a larger "gem" through the assembly of two or more smaller pieces of gem material. The repair process involves the reassembly of a broken gem through the application of a glue or adhesive to the adjoining break surfaces. In reconstruction, numerous small pieces, or even fine powders of similar material, are combined through the application of heat or pressure or both. In reconstruction, a binding agent may be used. In reconstruction, generally little care is used to match the individual pieces together well.

Surface Diffusion

This treatment is used primarily on pale-colored to colorless sapphires. Chemicals capable of producing a blue, red, orange, or pink color, or asterism are painted onto the surface of a pre-fashioned, near-colorless gem. The stone is then heated to a temperature approaching its melting point (2050°C). If the treatment is successful, the chemicals thermally diffuse into the stone's surface, resulting in the desired color enhancement. The treatment is superficial, generally 0.1 to 0.5 mm in depth, and the shallow color layer can be removed, or partially removed, by polishing or recutting. The color distribution is usually uneven with color concentrating along the girdle and facet junctions in a faceted gem, or at the girdle of a cabochon, as well as any pits or surface-reaching fractures. The high temperatures required for a successful diffusion process, and the chemicals involved, cause the pre-faceted or polished surfaces to become rough and corroded so that complete repolishing is necessary. Repolishing after treatment must be done very carefully as it reduces the diffused color layer and promotes further uneven color distribution. Diffusion-treated faceted stones are generally easier to detect than similarly treated cabochons. Because surface diffusion treatment is a form of high temperature heat treatment, all of the tell-tale microscopic features useful in detecting high-temperature treatment in sapphires and rubies may also be found in surface diffusion treated stones.

CONCLUSION

When buying or selling any "gem," a careful gemological examination is a necessity in accurately determining the nature and condition of that gemstone. After initially identifying a gem material, the questions that follow relate to differentiating natural from synthetic, and treated from untreated. It is wise to remember that a great number of gems have been treated in a wide variety of ways to improve their outward appearance. The more common treatments and their possible results, which are applicable to a wide variety of potential gem materials, together with some of their most important identifying features, have been presented in this chapter. Some of the similarities between completely natural gems and treated stones can be confusing and difficult to differentiate for those not trained in this gemological area. Sometimes the appearance of a stone may be the result of more than one type of treatment. For example, the surface-reaching cracks in a faceted "emerald" may be dyed as well as oiled, making it difficult to assess its true body color, and the apparent clarity improvement would probably cause problems in its valuation, as well.

Inclusions and the other microscopic features observed in gems, and an understanding of how these microfeatures react to the various treatment processes, provide important evidence in determining if a gemstone has been treated. But a much greater knowledge of inclusions, and other microscopic characteristics of both treated and untreated gemstones, is vitally necessary if we are to understand these processes better.

Gemstone treatment has been performed for centuries to make desirable gems more available to a larger number of consumers and virtually all treatment procedures are acceptable, as long as they are properly disclosed.

—*John I. Koivula and Thomas M. Moses*
Gemological Institute of America

index